Boxing Shadows

1500 Boxing

CU01032874

By Ralph Oates

LONDON LEAGUE PUBLICATIONS Ltd.

Boxing Shadows

1500 Boxing Quiz Questions

© Copyright Ralph Oates

The moral right of Ralph Oates to be identified as the author has been asserted.

Photographs provided by David Roake and Les Clark, and may not be reproduced without permission. Photographs for Photo Quiz questions 1 - 4 provided by David Roake, all others provided by Les Clark. All photos copyright to the photographer.

Editing, typesetting and layout by Peter Lush, with assistance from Dave Farrar and Graham Robertson.

This book is sold subject to the condition that it shall not, by way of trade or otherwise, be lent, resold, hired out or otherwise circulated without the publisher's prior consent in any form of binding or cover other than that in which it is published and without a similar condition including this condition being imposed on the subsequent purchaser.

A CIP catalogue record for this book is available from the British Library.

First published in Great Britain in September 1997 by:

London League Publications Ltd.
P.O. Box 10441
London E14 0SB

ISBN: 0-9526064-2-9

Cover design by:	Steven A. Spencer Illustration and Design 12, Yardley Way, Bradford, BD12 0JF
Silhouettes by:	Stephen McCarthy Graphic Design 23, Carol Street, London NW1 0HT
Printed and bound by:	Redwood Books, Trowbridge, Wiltshire.

Foreword

Ralph first came to my notice in the early 1960s when his name consistently appeared among the letters' pages of *Boxing News*. It seemed almost every week that he put his views forward and asked questions of the staff about the sport with great clarity and understanding. What it showed, of course, was his insatiable love of boxing that would not be extinguished down the years. In fact, it got stronger.

Our paths crossed following the publication of his first two books, *World Heavyweight Boxing Champions Elite* (1987) and *Know Your Boxing* (1991).The second title was one of the sport's first quiz books and was extremely well received, so much so that it was only a matter of time before there would be a further publication *Boxing Clever* duly arriving on the shelves in 1994.

Over the last three years, the former junior amateur boxer has become one of my right-hand men when it comes to putting the *British Boxing Board of Control Yearbook* to bed and, without trying to sound too patronising, his diligent work has been a godsend.

With his name now synonymous with boxing quiz books, Ralph's hard work deserves every further success, which I am confident that *Boxing Shadows* will provide, and hopefully, we will see many more titles come off the press under his banner.

Barry J. Hugman

Thank You

My thanks to Ruby Oates and Howard Oates for their assistance in checking the information in this book.

Ralph Oates

THE ESSENTIAL YEARBOOK FOR
EVERY BOXING FAN
and all those involved in the sport

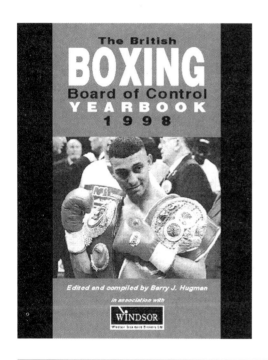

The British
BOXING
Board of Control
Y E A R B O O K
1 9 9 8

Edited and compiled by Barry J. Hugman
in association with
WINDSOR
Windsor Insurance Brokers Ltd

THE BRITISH
BOXING
BOARD OF CONTROL
YEARBOOK
1998

Edited by
BARRY HUGMAN

ORDER FORM

Please write clearly and in BLOCK CAPITALS

Please send me .... copy/copies of *The British Boxing Board of Control Yearbook 1998* @ £16.99

Name...

Address ....

....

....Post code ....

I wish to pay by Access/Visa/cheque the total amount of £.............

Delete as appropriate. All cheques payable to Queen Anne Press

Card no ⬚⬚⬚⬚⬚⬚⬚⬚⬚⬚⬚⬚⬚⬚⬚⬚ Card expiry date.............

Card holder's signature

Telephone credit card orders accepted on 01582 715866

Send orders to: Queen Anne Press, Windmill Cottage, Mackerye End, Harpenden, Herts AL5 5DR

Please allow 28 days for delivery. UK postage free – add £5 for overseas airmail postage.

Preface

There isn't anything quite like a quiz based on your favourite sport to stimulate those old brain cells. Indeed it can be great fun pitting your wits against a fellow boxing fan in a friendly competition.

However it is very difficult these days for followers of boxing to keep track of the many world title contests which take place and to know the name of the respective champions.

Most weight divisions have four title holders has recognised by the WBA, WBC, IBF and WBO. The nightmare does not end there, since there are other organisations which also stage World Championship bouts, so for someone not familiar with the sport attempting to find the true world title holder in any weight division must be like trying to catch shadows - boxing shadows.

The questions in this book are based on all the weight divisions. Some you will find easy, some you will find difficult. However I feel certain that you will find the book interesting with its many facts and figures. So go to your corners and come out fighting with the correct knockout answers.

Ralph Oates

Please note that every effort has been made to ensure that the information in this book is correct. However, the author and London league Publications Limited do not accept any liability for any loss sustained due to use of information contained in this book.

Interpretation of decisions

There is a difference in the interpretation of results between Great Britain and America. In this book, the British interpretation is used.

About the Author

This is Ralph Oates' fourth book about boxing. His previous books include *World Heavyweight Boxing Champions Elite*, *Know Your Boxing*, and *Boxing Clever*. He has also contributed to the *British Boxing Board of Control Yearbook*. *Boxing Shadows* took two years to complete. When not writing boxing books, Ralph works as a buyer for a national newspaper.

Sporting Club
LONSDALE
INTERNATIONAL

THE WORLD'S PREMIER CLUB OF SPORTS MEN & WOMEN SUPPORTING BOXING AT GRASS ROOTS LEVEL

President: The Earl Grey F.C.E.A.
Vice-President: Lord Addington
PATRONS: Reg Gutteridge OBE (UK)
Tom Pendry MP (UK) Angelo Dundee (USA)
Thomas Hauser (USA) Kepler Wessels (SA)
Joe Koizumi (JAPAN)

NEXT EVENT
British Boxing Awards Lunch in association with The British Boxing Board of Control and Barry Hugman's British Boxing Yearbook.

THURSDAY 2ND OCTOBER 1997

MILLENIUM MEMBERSHIP
NOW AVAILABLE

1997 ANNUAL MEMBERSHIP FEE WILL BE HELD UNTIL AT LEAST 2001. 1998 EVENTS INCLUDE INTERNATIONAL EX-BOXERS' CONVENTION (OVER 3 DAYS) IN CENTRAL LONDON.

For membership details and full fixture list write, phone or fax,
ALEX WHITE, CLUB ADMINISTRATOR, LONSDALE INTERNATIONAL SPORTING CLUB, 21 BEAK STREET, LONDON W1R 3LB
TEL: 44 (0) 171 434 1290
FAX: 44 (0) 171 734 2094
Every member receives exclusive membership card, club tie and club lapel badge.

CONTENTS

FOR WORLDWIDE BOXING COVERAGE
read

THE WORLD'S LEADING BOXING MAGAZINE

AVAILABLE FROM ALL GOOD NEWSAGENTS, PRICED £2.50

EACH ACTION-PACKED ISSUE FEATURES
BIG FIGHT ANALYSIS, RINGSIDE REPORTS,
INTERVIEWS WITH MAJOR BOXING STARS
& WORLD AND BRITISH BOXERS' RATINGS
ALL ILLUSTRATED BY AWARD-WINNING
COLOUR ACTION PHOTOGRAPHY

**TO RECEIVE 12 ISSUES POSTED RIGHT TO YOUR DOOR
AND MAKE SAVINGS ON OUR PROMOTED ISSUES,
INCLUDING OUR YEARLY BOXING CALENDAR,**

SUBSCRIBE TODAY

Send your cheque/PO, made payable to Boxing Monthly, to:

BOXING MONTHLY,
40 MORPETH ROAD, LONDON, E9 7LD

with your name, address, and which month's issue
you would like your subscription to start with

ANNUAL SUBSCRIPTION RATES   U.K. £30.00,

<u>OVERSEAS</u> - COPIES SENT BY AIRMAIL

EUROPE £40.00 (inc. Eire)

AMERICA £50.00 OR $75.00 (All airmail zone 1 countries)

AUSTRALIA, N.Z. £60.00 (All airmail zone 2 countries)

**FOR CREDIT CARD ORDERS RING 0181 986 4141
OR FAX 0181 986 4145, OR VISIT OUR WEB SITE AT
http://www.boxing-monthly.co.uk**

Preliminary Bouts

THE PRIZE RING

1. Prior to his entry to the prize ring, James Figg was a success at which other sport?
   A. Swimming B. Sword & Quarterstaff   C. Running

2. James Figg opened an academy devoted mostly to boxing.what was it called?
   A. Figg's Boxing Club B. The Fighters' Inn
   C. Figg's Amphitheatre

3. Which prize-fighter was called "The Deaf Un"?
   A. James Burke B. Jem Belcher C. Tom Allen

4. How tall was Daniel Mendoza?
   A. 5ft. 5in. B. 5ft. 6in. C. 5ft. 7in.

5. Which pugilist was elected a Member of Parliament for Pontefract in Yorkshire?
   A. John Gully B. Joe Goss C. John Jackson

6. Which one of the following spent a period of time in a debtors prison?
   A. Henry Pearce B. Tom Owen C. John Gully

7. What was Bendigo's real name?
   A. John Thompson B. Walter Thompson
   C. William Thompson

8.   Who did John L. Sullivan knockout in round nine on the 7th February 1882 to win the Bare-Knuckle World Heavyweight Title?
A. James Dalton B. Paddy Ryan
C. John Flood

9.   On the 10th March 1888 Charlie Mitchell challenged John L. Sullivan for the Heavyweight Crown and was given a draw over how many rounds?
A. 37 B. 38 C. 39

10.   John L.Sullivan defended his world title against Jake Kilrain on the 8th July 1889 and stopped him in which round?
A. 74 B. 75 C. 76

11.   In which part of America did the above contest take place?
A. New Orleans B. Richburg
C. Mississippi City

12.   Was the Sullivan - Kilrain encounter the last bare-knuckle contest for the world heavyweight title: *Yes or No?*

Answers: See page 38

2

WAS A WORLD CHAMPION

Which Boxer in each respective weight division **was** a World Champion?

Weight			
Heavy	Max Baer	Red Burman	Buddy Baer
Light-Heavy	Len Hutchins	Tommy Loughran	Jimmy Dupree
Middle	Tony Mundine	Jean-Claude Bouttier	Dick Tiger
Welter	Jean Josselin	Tony DeMarco	Marco Scano
Light	Chango Carmona	Joey Gibilisco	Charlie Nash
Feather	Mitsunori Seki	David Kotey	Toro George
Bantam	Manuel Ortiz	Sulley Shittu	Alan Rudkin
Fly	Benny Lynch	Fernando Atzori	Fritz Chervet

NOT A WORLD CHAMPION

Which Boxer in each respective Weight Division did **not** win a World Title?

Weight			
Heavy	Larry Holmes	John Tate	Randy "Tex" Cobb
Light-Heavy	Freddie Mills	Jorge Ahumada	Harold Johnson
Middle	Marcel Cerdan	Bennie Briscoe	Carl (Bobo) Olson
Welter	Billy Backus	Don Jordan	Pat Thomas
Light	Ray Mancini	Rodolfo Gonzalez	Dave Charnley
Feather	Shozo Saijo	Floyd Robertson	Salvador Sanchez
Bantam	Julian Solis	Lupe Pintor	Hugh Russell
Fly	Kelvin Smart	Shoji Oguma	Prudencio Cardona

Answers: See page 38

BOXING BOX I

The answer to each question will give you the name of a boxer. Use the first letter of the *surname* to fill in the blanks inside the *Boxing Box*. When completed you will find the name of a well known boxer.

1. Who was given a draw when he challenged Jack Johnson for the World Heavyweight Championship on 19 December 1913?

2. Who won the vacant WBA Cruiserweight Title on 13 February 1982 by outpointing Robbie Williams over fifteen rounds?

3. Who stopped Mike Weaver in round twelve in defence of his WBC Heavyweight Title on 22 June 1979?

4. Who did Arturo Frias knockout in round eight to win the WBA Lightweight Championship on 5 December 1981?

5. Who stopped Curtis Cokes in round thirteen on 18 April 1969 to win the World Welterweight Title?

6. Josefino Suarez was knocked out by which champion in ten rounds when he challenged for the WBC Bantamweight Title on 16 April 1994?

7. Who did Tony Canzoneri outpoint over fifteen rounds when contesting the World Lightweight Title on 10 May 1935?

8. Victor Galindez regained the WBA World Light-Heavyweight championship on 14 April 1979 when the defending title holder retired in round 9. Name the champion.

4

9.   Who did Nino Benvenuti knockout in six rounds to win the WBA Light-Middleweight crown on 18 June 1965?

10. Robert Gambini lost his European Light-Welterweight Title when he was outpointed over 12 rounds by which boxer?

11. James Cook retained his European Super-Middleweight Title on 22 October 1991 when which challenger retired in round 7?

12. Drew Docherty outpointed which future world featherweight champion over 8 rounds on 3 October 1990?

Answers: See page 38

Answers: See page 38

BOXING BOX II

Each answer will give you the name of a boxer. Use the first letter of the *Christian* name to fill the blanks inside the Boxing Box. You will then find the name of a well known boxer.

1. Who contested the WBC Welterweight title twice with Colin Jones in 1983?

2. For the World Lightweight title on 4 September 1946 Ronnie James was knocked out in 9 rounds by which champion?

3. Which former world champion outpointed Jim Watt over 15 rounds for British Lightweight Crown on 29 January 1973?

4. Ernie Terrell won the vacant WBA Heavyweight Title when he outpointed which opponent on 5 March 1965?

5. Who stopped James Douglas in round 10 on 30 May 1987 for the vacant IBF Heavyweight Crown?

6. Who, over 15 rounds, outpointed Eddie Avoth for the vacant European Light-Heavyweight Title on the 28th June 1969?

7. In contests for the World Heavyweight Title Floyd Patterson was knocked out twice in the first round by which opponent?

8. Who outpointed over 15 rounds Jeff Malcolm lost his Commonwealth Light-Welterweight title on 3 March 1979?

9. Who won the Heavyweight Gold Medal at the 1974 Commonwealth Games?

Answers: See page 38

6

TRUE OR FALSE

Respond to each question with a **true** or **false** answer.

1. During his career Eddie Avoth won both the British & Empire Light-Heavyweight Titles.

2. Gianfranco Rosi lost his first professional contest.

3. Barry McGuigan had six professional contests in 1984.

4. Barry McGuigan had seven professional contests in 1984.

5. During his career George Chuvalo held the Empire Heavyweight Title.

6. Lennox Lewis stopped Riddick Bowe in 2 rounds in the 1988 Olympic Games to win the Gold medal in the Super-Heavyweight Division.

7. At the same games Ray Mercer won Gold in the Heavyweight Division.

8. The 1992 Olympic Games were held in Italy.

9. The 1992 Olympic Games were held in Spain.

10. During his professional career Alan Minter held the British Light-Heavyweight Championship.

Answers: See page 39

ABA CHAMPIONS

In which year did the following boxers win an ABA title?.

Frank Bruno   Heavyweight
A. 1979 B. 1980 C. 1981

Jack Bodell   Light-Heavyweight
A. 1961 B. 1962 C. 1963

Mark Kaylor   Middleweight
A. 1978 B. 1979 C. 1980

Larry Paul   Light-Middleweight
A. 1971 B. 1972 C. 1973

Chris Pyatt   Welterweight
A. 1982 B. 1983 C. 1984

John H.Stracey   Light-Welterweight
A. 1967 B. 1968 C. 1969

Jim Watt   Lightweight
A. 1967 B. 1968. C. 1969

Kirkland Laing   Featherweight
A. 1970 B. 1971. C. 1972

Howard Winstone   Bantamweight
A. 1956 B. 1957 C. 1958

Walter McGowan   Flyweight
A. 1960 B. 1961 C. 1962

Answers: See page 39

BOXING RING I

Which Boxer **won** a world title on the date inside the ring?

```
Heavyweight

9 June 1978
```

A.   *Larry Holmes*
B.   *John Tate*
C.   *Mike Weaver*

```
Middleweight

16 March 1980
```

A.   *Marvin Hagler*
B.   *Alan Minter*
C.   *Vito Antuofermo*

```
Flyweight

14 June 1966
```

A.   *Berkrerk Chartvanchai*
B.   *Walter McGowan*
C.   *Efren Torres*

```
Featherweight

26 September
1964
```

A.   *Hogan Bassey*
B.   *Davey Moore*
C.   *Vicente Saldivar*

Answers: See page 39

BOXING RING II

Which Boxer **lost** a world title on the date in the ring?

WBC Light-Welterweight 29 January 1984

A. *Bruce Curry*
B. *Saoul Mamby*
C. *Gene Hatcher*

WBA Lightweight 1 June 1984

A. *Ernesto Espana*
B. *Ray Mancini*
C. *Livingstone Bramble*

WBA Super-Flyweight 18 September 1994

A. *Katsuya Onizuka*
B. *Julio Cesar Borboa*
C. *Jose Quirino*

WBA Light-Flyweight 18 November 1992

A. *Michael Carbajal*
B. *Hiroki Ioka*
C. *Humberto Gonzalez*

Answers: See page 39

IT'S A DRAW

7 of these World Title contests ended in a **draw**. Which ones?

1. Betulio Gonzalez vs Shoji Oguma (First contest)
   WBA Flyweight   *1979*

2. Chul-Ho Kim vs Raul Valdez
   WBC Super-Flyweight   *1982*

3. Miguel Lora vs Albert Davila
   WBC Bantamweight   *1988*

4. Welcome Ncita vs Jesus Rojas (First contest)
   IBF Super-Bantamweight *1991*

5. Jorge Paez. vs Louie Espinosa
   IBF Featherweight   *1989*

6. Azumah Nelson vs Jeff Fenech
   WBC Super-Featherweight *1991*

7. Mauricio Aceves vs Oscar Bejines
   WBO Lightweight   *1989*

8. Julio Cesar Chavez vs Roger Mayweather
   WBC Light-Welterweight *1989*

9. Simon Brown vs Jorge Vaca
   IBF Welterweight   *1988*

10. Eckhard Dagge vs Maurice Hope
    WBC Light-Middleweight *1977*

11. Iran Barkley vs Roberto Duran
    WBC Middleweight   *1989*

12. Sugar Ray Leonard vs Thomas Hearns
    WBC Super-Middleweight *1989*

13. Victor Galindez vs Yaqui Lopez
    WBA Light-Heavyweight   *1978*

14. Marvin Camel vs Mate Parlov
    Vacant WBC Cruiserweight *1979* *Answers: See page 39*

11

NAME THE COUNTRY

Name the country where these World Title contests took place.

1. Tommy Burns vs Gunner Moir
    Heavyweight   1907
    A. England B. America C. Canada

2. Georges Carpentier vs Battling Siki
    Light-Heavyweight   1922
    A. South Africa B. France C. England.

3. Rocky Graziano vs Tony Zale
    Middleweight   1948
    A. Italy B. America C. Mexico

4. Emile Griffith vs Brian Curvis
    Welterweight   1964
    A. America B. England C. Spain

5. Nicolino Loche vs Alfonso Frazer
    WBA Light-Welterweight   1972
    A. America B. Argentina C. Panama

6. Guts Ishimatsu vs Ken Buchanan
    WBC Lightweight   1975
    A. England B. Scotland C. Japan

7. Johnny Famechon vs Vicente Salidvar
    WBC Featherweight   1970
    A. Mexico B. Australia C. Italy

8. Ricardo Cardona vs Leo Randolph
    WBA Super-Bantamweight   1980
    A. Mexico B. Panama C. America

9. Lionel Rose vs Alan Rudkin
    Bantamweight   1969
    A. England B. Australia C. New Zealand

10. Walter McGowan vs Chartchai Chioni
    WBC Flyweight   1966
    A. Japan B. Scotland C. Thailand Answers: See page 40

NAME THE REFEREE

Name the referee of the following World Title contests.

1. Joe Louis vs Jack Roper   Heavyweight 1939
    A. Arthur Donovan B. George Blake
    C. Sam Hennessey

2. Joey Maxim vs Bob Murphy   Light-Heavyweight 1951
    A. Ruby Goldstein B. Johnny Burns C. Ray Miller

3. Gene Fuller vs Sugar Ray Robinson Middleweight 1960
    A. Harry Kessler B. Al Berl C. Tommy Hart

4. Maurice Hope vs Mike Baker
    WBC Light-Middleweight 1979
    A. Tony Perez B. Ray Baldeyrou C. David Pearl

5. Thomas Hearns vs Pablo Baez WBA Welterweight 1981
    A. Ken Morita B. Mills Lane C. Ismael Fernandez

6. Saoul Mamby vs Obisia Nwankpa
    WBC Light-Welterweight 1981
    A. Jack Keough B. Harry Gibbs C. Eddie Yoo

7. Jim Watt vs   Howard Davis Jr WBC Lightweight 1980
    A. Sid Nathan B. Larry Hazzard C. Carlos Padilla

8. Vicente Saldivar vs Howard Winstone Featherweight 1965
    A. Tommy Hart B. Bill Williams C. Roland Dakin

9. Carlos Zarate vs Lupe Pintor WBC Bantamweight 1979
    A. Mills Lane B. George Latka C. Carlos Berrocal

10. Miguel Canton vs Shoji Oguma
    Vacant WBC Flyweight 1975
    A. Rudy Ortega B. Ernest Magana C. Jay Edson

Answers: See page 40

WHICH ROUND

The challengers on the left hand side of the page won the world title by knocking out the defending champions in which round?

1.   Joe Louis vs James J. Braddock
   Heavyweight 1937   *A. 6 B. 7 C. 8*

2.   Jersey Joe Walcott vs Ezzard Charles
   Heavyweight 1951   *A. 7 B. 8 C. 9*

3.   Bob Foster vs Dick Tiger
   Light-Heavyweight 1968   *A. 4 B. 5 C. 6*

4.   Carlos Monzon V.Nino Benvenuti
   Middleweight 1970   *A. 10 B. 11 C. 12*

5.   Jimmy McLarnin vs Young Corbett III
   Welterweight 1933   *A. 1 B. 2 C. 3*

6.   Antonio Cervantes vs Alfonson Frazer
   WBA Light-Welterweight 1972   *A. 8 B. 9 C. 10*

7.   Ike Williams vs Juan Zurita
   Lightweight 1945   *A. 1 B. 2 C. 3*

8.   Ben Villaflor vs Kuniaki Shibata
   WBA Junior-Lightweight 1973   *A. 1 B. 2 C. 3*

9.   Clemente Sanchez vs Kuniaki Shibata
   WBC Featherweight 1972   *A. 1 B. 2 C. 3*

10.   Rafael Herrera vs Ruben Olivares
    Bantamweight 1972   *A. 7 B. 8 C. 9*

Answers: See page 40

14

BRITISH CHAMPIONS

Find the **weight** division in which the following Boxers held a **British** title.

1. Jimmy Anderson
2. Johnny Clark
3. Terry Downes
4. Larry Paul
5. Ernie Roderick
6. Billy Thompson
7. Jimmy Wilde
8. Bruce Woodcock

Heavyweight
Middleweight
Light-Middleweight
Welterweight
Lightweight
Junior-Lightweight (Now Super-Featherweight)
Bantamweight
Flyweight

Answers: See page 40

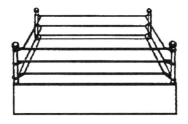

WHO'S THE BOXER?

Re-arrange the following to find well known Boxers.

1. OYR ONJSE
2. AHORDL YERG
3. XLENON SLWEI
4. LMGUIE LNEGA ZGNOAZEL
5. HCRSI KEUNBA
6. NPERELL HWTIKARE
7. KFARN OBUNR
8. LVRIGI LLHI
9. EKIFRNA ARNLLAD
10. OJLUI RCSAE ZCEHAV
11. ORCDRAI ZLPOE
12. XFLEI ADDIIRNT
13. LGENI NBEN
14. KICDDIR EBWO
15. HBREIE EDHI
16. EEVTS NOSNIRBO
17. YGRA JCABSO
18. EVETS SNICLLO
19. VIKEN KYEELL
20. EBBIOR AGARE

Answers: See page 40

16

QUICK FIRE BOXING ROUND

Answer each question with a **yes** or **no**.

1. Did Chris Finnegan once hold the British Middleweight title?

2. Did John H.Stracey once hold the WBA Welterweight title?

3. Did Willie Monroe outpoint Marvin Hagler over ten rounds in 1976?

4. Mike Spinks defended his WBA Light-Heavyweight title 4 times in 1982. Did each contest take place in Atlantic City?

5. Is it true that Sugar Ray Leonard stopped Thomas Hearns in round fourteen when they contested the undisputed World Welterweight title?

6. Did Aaron Pryor have eight contests in 1977?

7. Is it true that Edwin Rosario comes from Puerto Rico?

8. Did Roger Mayweather stop his first professional opponent Andrew Ruiz in the first round in 1981?

9. Is it true that Juan Laporte lost his first professional contest?

10. Did future World Flyweight King Santos Laciar lose a ten round points decision to Charlie Magri in 1980?

11. Was Charlie Magri a southpaw?

12. Did Terry Lawless manage Lloyd Honeyghan at the start of his professional career?

17

13. Did Barry McGuigan ever hold the British Super-Featherweight crown?

14. Did Paul Hodkinson have his first professional contest in America?

15. Did John Conteh ever box in Germany during his professional career?

16. Is it true that Gerrie Coetzee was once knocked out in the first round by Frank Bruno?

17. Is it true that Eusebio Pedroza had his first fifteen professional bouts in Panama City?

18. Did Tom Collins have his first professional contest in 1977?

19. Did Prince Rodney have his first professional contest in 1978?

20. Did Colin Jones ever box in Spain?

Answers: See page 41

NICK-NAMES

Find the nick-names of the following boxers.
(from both the past to the present)

1.   Riddick Bowe
     A. Big Daddy B. The Giant C. Mister Knockout

2.   Joe Brown
     A. The Master B. Mr.Boxing C. Old Bones

3.   Hector Camacho
     A. Mr.Smooth B. Macho Man C. The Mover

4.   Evander Holyfield
     A. The Real Deal B. The Big Deal C. The Dealer

5.   Jack Johnson
     A. The Galveston Giant B. Big Artha C. The Giant

6.   Stanley Ketchel
     A. The Fast One B. Michigan Assassin C. Mr.K.O.

7.   Jake La Motta
     A. The Wild Bull B. The Bronx Bull C. The Fast Bull

8.   Tommy Morrison.
     A. Mr.K.O. B. The Duke C. The King

9.   Willie Pep
     A. The Ghost B. Mr.Boxer C. Will O' The Wisp

10. Maxie Rosenbloom
     A. Slapsie Maxie B. The Smart One C. The Boxer

11. Bruce Seldon
    A. The Freight Train B. The Atlantic City Express
    C. The Power-Man

12. James Toney
    A. The Blaster B. Lights Out C. Mr.Knockout

13. Gene Tunney
    A. The Fighting Marine B. The Fighting Soldier
    C. One Punch Marine

14. Mickey Walker
    A. Toy Bulldog B. The Wilddog C. The Mad-Dog

15. Pernell Whitaker
    A. Class Boxer B. Sweet Pea C. Butter-Smooth

16. Jimmy Wilde
    A. Mr Big B. The Finisher C. Mighty Atom

17. Jess Willard
    A. The Giant B. Pottawatomie Giant C. Mr Big

18. Tim Witherspoon
    A. The Tim-Bomb B. Tim the K.O. C. Terrible Tim

19. Ad Wolgast
    A. Michigan Wildcat B. Michigan Blaster
    C. The Michigan Kid

20. Tony Zale
    A. The Steel-Man B. Mr Iron C. The Man of Steel

Answers: See page 41

PROMOTERS & MANAGERS

Find the Christian names of the following promoters and managers.

1. Arum   *A.* Paul *B.* Bob *C.* Steve

2. Brogan   *A.* John. *B.* Albert *C.* Pat

3. Conroy   *A.* Brenda *B.* Annette *C.* Katherine

4. Duff   *A.* Mickey *B.* Peter *C.* Frank

5. Gardiner   *A.* Ivor *B.* Douglas *C.* Dai

6. Gilmour Jr. *A.* Tommy *B.* Alan *C.* Harry

7. Griffin   *A.* Billy *B.* James *C.* Johnny

8. Hearn   *A.* John. *B.* Barry *C.* Keith

9. King   *A.* Don *B.* John. *C.* Paul.

10. Kushner   *A.* Jim *B.* Peter *C.* Cedric

11. Lawless   *A.* Terry *B.* Johnny *C.* Jimmy

12. Lewis   *A.* Tom *B.* Butch *C.* Adam

13. Maloney   *A.* David *B.* Frank *C.* Don

14. Morrison   *A.* Janet *B.* Anne *C.* Katherine

15. Palle   *A.* Kurt *B.* Mogens *C.* Borg

16. Rushton   *A.* Christine *B.* Joan *C.* Paula

17. Sauerland   *A.* Franz *B.* Karl *C.* Wilfried

18. Segal   *A.* Barry *B.* Mike *C.* John.

19. Steene   *A.* Tom *B.* Adam *C.* Greg

20. Trickett   *A.* Jack *B.* Larry *C.* Alan

Answers: See page 41

FIND THE SOUTHPAW

Ten of the listed below box in the southpaw stance. Name them.

1.   Dennis Andries
2.   Johnny Armour
3.   Riddick Bowe
4.   Eddie Cook
5.   Chris Eubank
6.   Prince Naseem Hamed
7.   Thomas Hearns
8.   Herbie Hide
9.   Thierry Jacob
10. Gary Jacobs
11. Hiroshi Kawashima
12. Kevin Kelley
13. Lennox Lewis
14. Michael Moorer
15. Steve Robinson
16. Mike Tyson
17. Julio Cesar Vasquez
18. Paul Weir
19. Richie Wenton
20. Pernell Whitaker

Answers: See page 42

FIND THE LADY

1. Who was the first female Scottish promoter?
    *A. Annette Conroy B. Katherine Morrison
    C. Tania Follett*

2. Who was the first woman second in British boxing?
    A. Lisa Budd B. Katherine Morrison C. Tania Follett

3. Which lady is a boxing manager?
    A. Carol Polis B. Eva Shain C. Jackie Kallen

4. Which lady was the first female judge to be appointed in
    America?
    A. Eugenia Williams B. Eva Shain C. Carol Polis

5. Who was the first British female MC?
    A. Tania Follett B. Lisa Budd C. Annette Conroy

6. When Chris Eubank enters the ring he does so with the song
    "Simply The Best" being played. Who is the singer?
    A. Cher B. Whitney Houston C. Tina Turner

7. Who was the first lady to be a judge at a World
    Heavyweight Title contest?
    A. Carol Polis B. Eva Shain C. Patricia Jarman

8. Which lady is a referee?
    A. Carol Polis B. Gwen Adair C. Eva Shain

9. Who was the first female promoter in the north east of
    England?
    *A. Katherine Morrison B. Annette Conroy
    C. Tania Follett*

10. When Riddick Bowe defended his World Heavyweight crown against Jesse Ferguson, three women were appointed to judge the contest. Sheila Harmon-Martin and Patricia Jarman were two of them, who was the third?
   A. Carol Polis   B. Eugenia Williams   C. Debra Barnes

11. When Mike Dokes won the WBA version of the World Heavyweight title by stopping holder Mike Weaver in the first round on 10 December 1982 a female judge was in attendance. Who was she?
   A. Carol Polis   B. Eva Shain   C. Carol Castellano

12. In 1997, who became British boxing's first lady manager?
   A. Lisa Budd   B. Tania Follett   C. Annette Conroy

Answers: See page 42

REAL NAMES

Many Boxers change their name when they embark upon a career in the ring. Find the **real name** of the following:

1.   Mushy Callahan
     *A. Henry Jackson B. Vincent Morris Scheer
     C. Judah Bergman*

2.   Young Corbett II
     A. Sidney Walker B. Verlin Jenks C. William H.Rothwell

3.   Johnny Dundee.
     A. Giuseppe Carrora B. Sidney Walker C. Sabino Ferullo

4.   Jackie Fields
     A. Benjamin Leiner B. Janos Ruthaly C. Jacob Finkelstein

5.   Sammy Fuller
     *A.Arnold Raymond Cream B. Eligio Sardinias
     C. Sabino Ferullo*

6.   Joey Giardello
     *A. Carmine Orlando Tilelli B. Richard Ihetu
     C. Gershon Mendeloff*

7.   Rocky Graziano
     *A.Samuel Engotti B. Arnold Lee Wright
     C. Thomas Rocco Barbella*

8.   Beau Jack
     *A. Sidney Walker B. Henry Jackson
     C. Frederick Hall Thomas*

9.   Ben Jeby
     *A. Morris Jebaltowski B. Antonio Pilleteri
     C. Walker Smith Jr*

10. Lew Jenkins
     *A. Edward Patrick Walker B. Gerardo Gonzalez
     C. Verlin Jenks*

11. Tippy Larkin
    A. *Vincent Morris Scheer* **B.** *Antonio Pilleteri*
    C. *Janos Ruthaly*

12. Benny Leonard
    A. *Benjamin Leiner* **B.** *Rocco Francis Marchegiano*
    C. *Richard Ihetu*

13. Rocky Marciano
    A. *Thomas Rocco Barbella* **B.** *Giuseppe Carrora*
    C. *Rocco Francis Marchegiano*

14. Sugar Ray Robinson
    A. *Sidney Walker* **B.** *Walker Smith Jr* **C.** *Verlin Jenks*

15. Battling Siki.
    A. *Louis Phal* **B.** *Benjamin Leiner* **C.** *Gershom Mendeloff*

16. Dick Tiger
    A. *Richard Ihetu* **B.** *Walker Smith Jr* **C.** *Samuel Engotti*

17. Mickey Walker
    A. *Walker Smith Jr* **B.** *Edward Patrick Walker*
    C. *Sidney Walker*

18. Freddie Welsh
    A. *Joseph Francis Hagen* **B.** *Frederick Hall Thomas*
    C. *Jacob Finkelstein*

19. Jersey Joe Walcott
    A. *Arnold Raymond Cream* **B.** *Gerardo Gonzalez*
    C. *Sabino Ferullo*

20. Tony Zale
    A. *Janos Ruthaly* **B.** *Archibald Lee Wright*
    C. *Anthony Florian Zaleski*

Answers: See page 42

FIND THE REFEREE'S NAME

Find the Christian name of the following referees:

1.	Battle	*A. Rudy B. Joe C. Mickey*
2.	Byrd	*A. Marty B. Mike C. Robert*
3.	Cowsill	*A. Paul B. Roy C. Phil*
4.	Coyle	*A. Toby B. John C. Steve*
5.	Denkin	*A. Toby B. Marty C. Mills*
6.	Francis	*A. Richard B. Roy C. Reg*
7.	Gibson	*A. Toby B. Robert C. Stanley*
8.	Halpern	*A. Mitch B. Paul C. Mickey*
9.	Heatherwick	*A. Paul. B. Roy C. Mike*
10.	Hutcheon	*A. Al B. Paul C. Mike*
11.	Lane	*A. Steve B. Mills C. Al*
12.	Lewis	*A. Steve B. Roy C. Denzil.*
13.	O'Neil	*A. Denzil B. Joe C. Mitch*
14.	Smoger	*A. Phil B. Mills C. Steve*
15.	Snowball	*A. Christodolou B. Wally C. Mickey*
16.	Steele	*A. Steve B. Richard C. Paul*
17.	Thomas	*A. Paul B. Steve C. Toby*
18.	Thompson	*A. Stanley B. Steve C. Reg*
19.	Vann	*A. Barney B. Mickey C. Marty*
20.	Wilson	*A. Denzil B. Barney C. Reg*

Answers: See page 42

HOW MANY PROFESSIONAL BOUTS

How many professional bouts did the following boxers have during their careers?

1. Muhammad Ali   *A. 59 B. 60 C. 61*

2. Nino Benvenuti   *A. 89 B. 90 C. 91*

3. John Caldwell   *A. 35 B. 36 C. 37*

4. John Conteh   *A. 39 B. 40 C. 41.*

5. Terry Downes   *A. 42 B. 43 C. 44*

6. Johnny Famechon   *A. 65 B. 66 C. 67*

7. Gene Fuller   *A. 63 B. 64 C. 65*

8. Maurice Hope   *A. 35 B. 36 C. 37*

9. Alan Minter   *A. 47 B. 48 C. 49*

10. Carlos Monzon   *A. 100 B. 101 C. 102*

11. Walter McGowan   *A. 40 B. 41 C. 42*

12. Willie Pastrano   *A. 82 B. 83 C. 84*

13. Willie Pep   *A. 241 B. 242 C. 243*

14. John H.Stracey   *A. 51 B. 52 C. 53*

15. Sugar Ray Robinson *A. 201 B. 202 C. 203*

16. Marcel Thil   *A. 95 B. 96 C. 97*

17. Gene Tunney   *A. 75 B. 76 C. 77*

18. Jim Watt   *A. 45 B. 46 C. 47*

19. Howard Winstone   *A. 67 B. 68 C. 69*

20. Tony Zale   *A. 86 B. 87 C. 88*

Answers: See page 43

FIRST PROFESSIONAL DEFEAT

Who was the first man to **defeat** the following Boxers in the professional ranks?

1. Dennis Andries
    A. Bunny Johnson B. Bonny Mckenzie C. Mustafa Wasajja

2. Nigel Benn
    A. Chris Eubank B. Michael Watson
    C. Sanderline Williams

3. John Conteh
    A. Eddie Duncan B.Mate Parlov C. Matt Saad Muhammad

4. Alberto Davila
    A. Eliseo Cosme B. Raul Tirado C. Cecil Escobido

5. George Foreman
    A. Jimmy Young B. Muhammad Ali C. Evander Holyfield

6. Gene Hatcher.
    A. Tyrone Crawley B. Alfredo Escalera
    C. Lloyd Honeyghan

7. Larry Holmes
    A. Mike Tyson B. Michael Spinks C. Evander Holyfield

8. Lloyd Honeyghan
    A. Jorge Vaca B. Marlon Starling C. Mark Breland

9. Lennox Lewis
    A. Tony Tucker B. Phil Jackson C. Oliver McCall

10. Rocky Lockridge
    A. Juan Laporte B. Eusebio Pedroza C. Jose Nieto

11. Charlie Magri
   A. Jose Torres B. Juan Diaz C. Frank Cedeno

12. Ray Mancini
   A. Alexis Arguello B. Jose Luis Ramirez
   C. Livingstone Bramble

13. Alan Minter
   A. Jan Magdziarz B. Don McMillan C. Ricky Ortiz

14. Greg Page
   A. David Bey B. Tim Witherspoon C. Trevor Berbick

15. Jose Luis Ramirez
   A. Ruben Olivares B. Alexis Arguello C. Ray Mancini

16. Steve Robinson
   A. Marcel Herbert B. Nicky Lucas C. Mark Bates

17. Leon Spinks
   A. Muhammad Ali B. Larry Holmes C. Carlos De Leon

18. Michael Spinks
   A. Eddie Davis B. Mike Tyson C. John Davis

19. Mike Tyson.
   A. Razor Ruddock B. James "Buster" Douglas
   C. Tony Tucker

20. Jiro Watanabe
   A. Chulho Kim B. Luis Ibanez C. Tito Abella

Answers: See page 43

FIRST PROFESSIONAL OPPONENT

Who was the **first** professional opponent for the following Boxers?

1. Dennis Andries
    A. Ray Pearce B. Mark Seabrook C. Ken Jones

2. Nigel Benn.
    A. Kevin Roper B. Graeme Ahmed C. Bob Niewenhuizen

3. Pat Clinton
    A. Des Gargano B. Gordon Stobie C. George Bailey

4. Gerrie Coetzee
    A. Bert Cuipers B. Steve Foley C. Chris Roos

5. Roberto Duran
    A. Carlos Mendoza B. Juan Gondola C. Enrique Jacobo

6. Alberto Davila
    A. Ruben Mozqueda B. Carlos Villareal C. Thomas Huerta

7. Chris Eubank
    A. Mike Bragwell B. Kenny Cannida C. Tim Brown

8. Jaime Garza
    A. Eduardo Villareal B. Francisco Silva
    C. Miguel Bejarno

9. Marvin Hagler
    A. Sonny Williams B. Terry Ryan C. Muhammad Smith

10. Thomas Hearns
    A. Jerome Hill B. Willie Wren C. Jerry Strickland

11. Larry Holmes
    A. *Art Savage* **B.** *Don Branch* **C.** *Rodell Dupree*

12. Juan Laporte.
    A. *John Green* **B.** *Jerry Strickland* **C.** *Santos Cruz*

13. Roger Mayweather.
    A. *Javier Benitez* **B.** *Andrew Ruiz* **C.** *Jaime Nava*

14. Lupe Madera.
    A. *Victor Canul* **B.** *Ranulfo Canto* **C.** *Jesus Herrara*

15. Alan Minter.
    A. *John Lowe* **B.** *Anton Schnedi* **C.** *Maurice Thomas*

16. Claude Noel.
    A. *Art De Freitas* **B.** *Clive Nichols* **C.** *Len Blackmore*

17. Patrizio Oliva
    A. *Georges Cotin* **B.** *Rene Martin* **C.** *Nelson Gomez*

18. Eusebio Pedroza
    A. *Julio Garcia* **B.** *Jose Santana* **C.** *Jorge Bernal*

19. Michael Spinks
    A. *Luis Rodriguez* **B.** *"Hot Dog" Benson* **C.** *Joe Borden*

20. Jim Watt
    A. *Alex Gibson* **B.** *Victor Paul* **C.** *Santos Martin*

Answers: See page 43

LAST PROFESSIONAL OPPONENT

Who did the following Boxers meet in their **last** professional contest?

1. Muhammad Ali
   A. Trevor Berbick B. Larry Holmes C. Leon Spinks

2. Johnny Bratton
   A. Chico Varona B. Johnny Saxton C. Del Flanagan

3. James J.Corbett
   *A. Charlie (Kid) McCoy B. James J.Jeffries
   C. Tom Sharkey*

4. Jack Dempsey
   A. Gene Tunney B. Jack Sharkey C. Eli Stanton

5. George Dixon
   A. Billy Ryan B. Harry Shea C. Monk The Newsboy

6. Gene Fuller
   A. Benny Paret B. Dick Tiger C. Sugar Ray Robinson

7. Emile Griffith
   A. Alan Minter B. Joel Bonnetaz C. Christy Elliott

8. Maurice Hope
   A. Wilfred Benitez B. Luigi Minchillo C. Carlos Herrera

9. Jack Johnson
   A. Bill Hartwell B. Bob Lawson C. Homer Smith

10. Don Jordan
    A. Joey Limas B. Chivo Diaz C. Battling Torres

11. Frankie Klick
    A. Al Citrino B. Clever Henry C. Felix Garcia

12. Benny Lynch
    A. Kayo Morgan B. Aurel Toma C. Jackie Jurich

13. Joey Maxim
    A. Ulli Ritter B. Mino Bozzano C. Heinz Neuhaus

14. Carlos Monzon
    A. Gratien Tonna B. Tony Licata C. Rodrigo Valdez

15. Ken Overlin
    A. R.J.Lewis B. Paul Hartneck C. Al Labos

16. Willie Pep
    A. Ray Coleman B. Tommy Haden C. Calvin Woodland

17. Sandy Saddler
    A. Larry Boardman B. Flash Elorde C. Joe Lopes

18. Mickey Walker
    A. Eric Seelig B. Red Bush C. Irish Eddie

19. Ike Williams
    A. Bea Jack B. Jed Black C. Billy Andy

20. Chalky Wright
    A. Willie Pep B. Ernie Hunick C. Johnny Dell

Answers: See page 44

FIRST PROFESSIONAL YEAR

When did the following Boxers make their professional **debut**?

1.	Muhammad Ali	*A. 1959 B. 1960 C. 1961*
2.	Carmen Basilio	*A. 1947 B. 1948 C. 1949*
3.	Nino Benvenuti	*A. 1961 B. 1962 C. 1963*
4.	Ken Buchanan	*A. 1963 B. 1964 C. 1965*
5.	John Conteh	*A. 1970. B. 1971. C. 1972.*
6.	Terry Downes	*A. 1956 B. 1957 C. 1958*
7.	Ralph Dupas	*A. 1950 B. 1951 C. 1952*
8.	Roberto Duran	*A. 1965 B. 1966 C. 1967*
9.	Jimmy Ellis	*A. 1961 B. 1962 C. 1963*
10.	Ernesto Espana	*A. 1973 B. 1974 C. 1975*
11.	Johnny Famechon	*A. 1960 B. 1961 C. 1962*
12.	Bob Foster	*A. 1961 B. 1962 C. 1963*
13.	Joe Frazier	*A. 1963 B. 1964 C. 1965*
14.	Victor Galindez	*A. 1969 B. 1970 C. 1971*
15.	Emile Griffith	*A. 1957 B. 1958 C. 1959*
16.	Marvin Hagler	*A. 1971 B. 1972 C. 1973*
17.	Larry Holmes	*A. 1973 B. 1974 C. 1975*
18.	Carlos Monzon.	*A. 1962 B. 1963 C. 1964*
19.	Jim Watt	*A. 1966 B. 1967 C. 1968*
20.	Howard Winstone	*A. 1958 B. 1959 C. 1960*

Answers: See page 44

LAST PROFESSIONAL YEAR

When was the following Boxers' **last** professional appearance?

1.	Terry Allen	*A. 1954 B. 1955 C. 1956*
2.	Abe Attell	*A. 1915 B. 1916 C. 1917*
3.	Jack (Kid) Berg	*A. 1944 B. 1945 C. 1946*
4.	Joe Brown	*A. 1969 B. 1970 C. 1971*
5.	Johnny Caldwell	*A. 1965 B. 1966 C. 1967*
6.	Marcel Cerdan	*A. 1947 B. 1948 C. 1949*
7.	Vince Dundee	*A. 1937 B. 1938 C. 1939*
8.	Bob Fitzsimmons	*A. 1912 B. 1913 C. 1914*
9.	Joey Giardello	*A. 1967 B. 1968 C. 1969*
10.	Rocky Graziano	*A. 1951 B. 1952 C. 1953*
11.	Archie Moore	*A. 1963 B. 1964 C. 1965*
12.	Bob Olin	*A. 1938 B. 1939 C. 1940*
13.	Floyd Patterson	*A. 1970 B. 1971 C. 1972*
14.	Leo Rodak	*A. 1946 B. 1947 C. 1948*
15.	Gustave Roth	*A. 1944 B. 1945 C. 1946*
16.	John H.Stracey	*A. 1978 B. 1979 C. 1980*
17.	Randolph Turpin	*A. 1962 B. 1963 C. 1964*
18.	Pancho Villa	*A. 1924 B. 1925 C. 1926*
19.	Ike Williams	*A. 1953 B. 1954 C. 1955*
20.	Tony Zale	*A. 1948 B. 1949 C. 1950*

Answers: See page 44

NATIONALITY

From which country do the following boxers originate?

1.	Yuri Arbachakov	*A. France* *B. Russia* *C. Spain*
2.	Riddick Bowe	*A. America* *B. Russia* *C. Spain*
3.	Simon Brown	*A. England* *B. Korea* *C. Jamaica*
4.	Frank Bruno	*A. Jamaica* *B. England* *C. Canada*
5.	Hector Camacho	*A. Dominican Republic* *B. Mexico* *C. Puerto Rico*
6.	Ray Close	*A. Ireland* *B. Scotland* *C. Wales*
7.	Juan Martin Coggi	*A. Germany* *B. Argentina* *C. Mexico*
8.	Humberto Gonzalez	*A. Colombia* *B. Philippines* *C. Mexico*
9.	David Griman	*A. Venezuela* *B. Panama* *C. Mexico*
10.	David Izeqwire	*A. Australia* *B. Nigeria* *C. Taiwan*
11.	Gary Jacobs	*A. Wales* *B. England* *C. Scotland.*
12.	Henry Maske	*A. Germany* *B. France* *C. Austria*
13.	Azumah Nelson	*A. Nigeria* *B. Ghana* *C. Jamaica*
14.	Welcome Ncita	*A. South Africa.* *B. Ghana* *C. Nigeria*
15.	Tony Pep	*A. Canada.* *B. America* *C. Australia*
16.	Steve Robinson	*A. Scotland.* *B. England* *C. Wales*
17.	Gianfranco Rosi	*A. Spain.* *B. France* *C. Italy*
18.	Fabrice Tiozzo	*A. France* *B. Spain* *C. Germany*
19.	Regilio Tuur	*A. Kenya* *B. Korea* *C. Netherlands*
20.	Yasuei Yakushiji	*A. Thailand* *B. Colombia* *C. Japan*

Answers: See page 45

ANSWERS

THE PRIZE RING

1. Sword & Quarterstaff
2. Figg's Amphitheatre
3. James Burke
4. 5ft. 7 inches
5. John Gully
6. John Gully
7. William Thompson
8. Paddy Ryan
9. 39
10. 75
11. Richburg
12. Yes

WAS A WORLD CHAMPION

Weight	
Heavy	Max Baer
Light-Heavy	Tommy Loughran
Middle	Dick Tiger
Welter	Tony DeMarco
Light	Chango Carmona
Feather	David Kotey
Bantam	Manuel Ortiz
Fly	Benny Lynch

NOT A WORLD CHAMPION

Weight	
Heavy	Randy "Tex" Cobb
Light-Heavy	Jorge Ahumada
Middle	Bennie Briscoe

Welter	Pat Thomas
Light	Dave Charnley
Feather	Floyd Robertson
Bantam	Hugh Russell
Fly	Kelvin Smart

BOXING BOX I

1.	Jim Johnson	J
2.	Ossie Ocasio	O
3.	Larry Holmes	H
4.	Claude Noel	N
5.	Jose Napoles	N
6.	Yasuei Yakushiji	Y
7.	Lou Ambers	A
8.	Mike Rossman	R
9.	Sandro Mazzinghi	M
10.	Patrizio Oliva	O
11.	Tarmo Uusiverta	U
12.	Steve Robinson	R

BOXING BOX II

1.	Milton McCrory	M
2.	Ike Williams	I
3.	Ken Buchanan	K
4.	Eddie Machen	E
5.	Tony Tucker	T
6.	Yvan Prebeg	Y
7.	Sonny Liston	S
8.	Obisia Nwankpa	O
9.	Neville Meade	N

TRUE OR FALSE

1. TRUE
2. FALSE
3. TRUE
4. FALSE
5. FALSE
6. TRUE
7. TRUE
8. FALSE
9. TRUE
10. FALSE

ABA CHAMPIONS

Frank Bruno	1980
Jack Bodell	1961
Mark Kaylor	1980
Larry Paul	1972
Chris Pyatt	1982
John H.Stracey	1969
Jim Watt	1968
Kirkland Laing	1972
Howard Winstone	1958
Walter McGowan	1961

BOXING RING I

Heavyweight Larry Holmes
Middleweight Alan Minter
Flyweight Walter McGowan
Featherweight Vicente Saldivar

BOXING RING II

WBC Light-Welterweight
Bruce Curry
WBA Lightweight
Ray Mancini
WBA Super-Flyweight
Katsuya Onizuka
WBA Light-Flyweight
Hiroki Ioka

IT'S A DRAW

1. Betulio Gonzalez vs Shoji Oguma
WBA Flyweight 1979

2. Chul-Ho Kim vs Raul Valdez.
WBC Super-Flyweight 1982

5. Jorge Paez vs Louie Espinosa.
IBF Featherweight 1989

6. Azumah Nelson vs Jeff Fenech
WBC Super- Featherweight 1991

10. Eckhard Dagge vs Maurice Hope
WBC Light-Middleweight 1977

12. Sugar Ray Leonard vs Thomas Hearns
WBC Super-Middleweight 1989

14. Marvin Camel vs Mate Parlov
Vacant WBC Cruiserweight 1979

NAME THE COUNTRY

1. England
2. France
3. America
4. England
5. Panama
6. Japan
7. Italy
8. America
9. Australia
10. Thailand

NAME THE REFEREE

1. George Blake
2. Ruby Goldstein
3. Tommy Hart
4. Ray Baldeyrou
5. Ken Morita
6. Harry Gibbs
7. Carlos Padilla
8. Bill Williams
9. Mills Lane
10. Jay Edson

WHICH ROUND

1. Eight
2. Seven
3. Four
4. Twelve
5. One
6. Ten
7. Two
8. One
9. Three
10. Eight

BRITISH CHAMPIONS

1. Jimmy Anderson
   Junior-Lightweight
2. Johnny Clark *Bantamweight*
3. Terry Downes *Middleweight*
4. Larry Paul
   Light-Middleweight
5. Ernie Roderick *Welterweight*
6. Billy Thompson *Lightweight*
7. Jimmy Wilde *Flyweight*
8. Bruce Woodcock
   Heavyweight

WHO'S THE BOXER

1. Roy Jones
2. Harold Grey
3. Lennox Lewis
4. Miguel Angel Gonzalez
5. Chris Eubank
6. Pernell Whitaker
7. Frank Bruno
8. Virgil Hill
9. Frankie Randall
10. Julio Cesar Chavez
11. Ricardo Lopez
12. Felix Trinidad
13. Nigel Benn
14. Riddick Bowe
15. Herbie Hide
16. Steve Robinson
17. Gary Jacobs
18. Steve Collins
19. Kevin Kelley
20. Robbie Regan

QUICK FIRE BOXING ROUND

1. No
2. No
3. Yes
4. Yes
5. Yes
6. Yes
7. Yes
8. Yes
9. No
10. Yes
11. No
12. Yes
13. No
14. No
15. No
16. Yes
17. Yes
18. Yes
19. No
20. No

NICK-NAMES

1. Big Daddy
2. Old Bones
3. Macho Man
4. The Real Deal
5. The Galveston Giant
6. Michigan Assassin
7. The Bronx Bull
8. The Duke
9. Will O' Wisp
10. Slapsie Maxie

11. The Atlantic City Express
12. Lights Out
13. The Fighting Marine
14. Toy Bulldog
15. Sweet Pea
16. Mighty Atom
17. Pottawatomie Giant
18. Terrible Tim
19. Michigan Wildcat
20. The Man Of Steel

PROMOTERS & MANAGERS

1. Bob
2. Pat
3. Annette
4. Mickey
5. Dai
6. Tommy
7. Johnny
8. Barry
9. Don
10. Cedric
11. Terry
12. Butch
13. Frank
14. Katherine
15. Mogens
16. Christine
17. Wilfried
18. Mike
19. Greg
20. Jack

FIND THE SOUTHPAW

2. Johnny Armour
4. Eddie Cook
6. Prince Naseem Hamed
9. Thierry Jacob
10. Gary Jacobs
11. Hiroshi Kawashima
12. Kevin Kelley
14. Michael Moorer
17. Julio Cesar Vasquez
20. Pernell Whitaker

FIND THE LADY

1. Katherine Morrison
2. Tania Follett
3. Jackie Kallen
4. Carol Polis
5. Lisa Budd
6. Tina Turner
7. Eva Shain
8. Gwen Adair
9. Annette Conroy
10. Eugenia Williams
11. Carol Polis
12. Tania Follett

REAL NAMES

1. Vincent Morris Scheer
2. William H.Rothwell
3. Giuseppe Carrora
4. Jacob Finkelstein
5. Sabino Ferullo
6. Carmine Orlando Tilelli
7. Thomas Rocco Barbella
8. Sidney Walker
9. Morris Jebaltowski
10. Verlin Jenks
11. Antonio Pilleteri
12. Benjamin Leiner
13. Rocco Francis Marchegiano
14. Walker Smith Jr
15. Louis Phal
16. Richard Ihetu
17. Edward Patrick Walker
18. Frederick Hall Thomas
19. Arnold Raymond Cream
20. Anthony Florian Zaleski

FIND THE REFEREE'S NAME

1. Rudy
2. Robert
3. Phil
4. John
5. Marty
6. Roy
7. Toby
8. Mitch
9. Mike
10. Al
11. Mills
12. Denzil
13. Joe.
14. Steve
15. Wally
16. Richard
17. Paul.
18. Reg
19. Mickey
20. Barney

HOW MANY
PROFESSIONAL BOUTS

1. 61
2. 90
3. 35
4. 39
5. 44
6. 67
7. 64
8. 35
9. 49
10. 102
11. 40
12. 84
13. 242
14. 51
15. 201
16. 97
17. 77
18. 46
19. 67
20. 87

FIRST PROFESSIONAL
DEFEAT

1. Bonny Mckenzie
2. Michael Watson
3. Eddie Duncan
4. Cecil Escobido
5. Muhammad Ali
6. Tyrone Crawley
7. Michael Spinks
8. Jorge Vaca
9. Oliver McCall
10. Eusebio Pedroza
11. Juan Diaz

12. Alexis Arguello
13. Don McMillan
14. Trevor Berbick
15. Ruben Olivares
16. Nicky Lucas
17. Muhammad Ali
18. Mike Tyson
19. James "Buster" Douglas
20. Chulho Kim

FIRST PROFESSIONAL
OPPONENT

1. Ray Pearce
2. Graeme Ahmed
3. Gordon Stobie
4. Chris Roos
5. Carlos Mendoza
6. Carlos Villareal
7. Tim Brown
8. Eduardo Villareal
9. Terry Ryan
10. Jerome Hill
11. Rodell Dupree
12. John Green
13. Andrew Ruiz
14. Victor Canul
15. Maurice Thomas
16. Art De Freitas
17. Nelson Gomez
18. Julio Garcia
19. "Hot Dog" Benson
20. Santos Martin

LAST PROFESSIONAL OPPONENT

1. Trevor Berbick
2. Del Flanagan
3. James J.Jeffries
4. Gene Tunney
5. Monk The Newsboy
6. Dick Tiger
7. Alan Minter
8. Luigi Minchillo
9. Bill Hartwell
10. Battling Torres
11. Al Citrino
12. Aurel Toma
13. Ulli Ritter
14. Rodrigo Valdez
15. R.J.Lewis
16. Calvin Woodland
17. Larry Boardman
18. Red Bush
19 Bea Jack
20. Ernie Hunick

FIRST PROFESSIONAL YEAR

1. 1960
2. 1948
3. 1961
4. 1965
5. 1971
6. 1957
7. 1950
8. 1967
9. 1961
10. 1975
11. 1961
12. 1961
13. 1965
14. 1969
15. 1958
16. 1973
17. 1973
18. 1963
19. 1968
20. 1959

LAST PROFESSIONAL YEAR

1. 1954
2. 1917
3. 1945
4. 1970
5. 1965
6. 1949
7. 1937
8. 1914
9. 1967
10. 1952
11. 1965
12. 1939
13. 1972
14. 1946
15. 1945
16. 1978
17. 1964
18. 1925
19. 1955
20. 1948

44

NATIONALITY

1. Russia
2. America
3. Jamaica
4. England
5. Puerto Rico
6. Ireland
7. Argentina
8. Mexico
9. Venezuela
10. Nigeria
11. Scotland
12. Germany
13. Ghana
14. South Africa
15. Canada
16. Wales
17. Italy
18. France
19. Netherlands
20. Japan

Rugby League and Cricket Books

The Sin Bin

A new collection of Rugby League cartoons and humour. Caricatures of leading people in the game ... the Adventures of Mo ... The Flatcappers... Bath v Wigan ... Life Down South ... and much more.

Price: £5.95. Published in October 1996.

From Arundel to Zimbabwe
A Cricket Followers' Guide to British and Internatonal Cricket Grounds

Includes details of ground facilities, price discounts, road directions and public transport information. Published in April 1997. Over 30 photos. **Excellent value at £6.50.**

Touch and Go
A History of Professional Rugby League in London

From the clubs in the 1930s to the London Broncos. Includes all the international matches played in London, and the first Wembley Cup Final. Interviews with key people involved in Fulham, London Crusaders and the Broncos. Many photos and illustrations, and comprehensive statistics. **Published August 1995. 380 pages for just £9.00.**

To order any of the above books, make cheques payable to: London League Publications Ltd, and send to: London League Publications Ltd, PO Box 10441, London E14 0SB. Special offers for readers of this book: All books post free. Order all three books for only £18.00

The Photo Quiz

Name the boxers in these photos

1.

Born 15 October 1858
Middle name: Lawrence
Height 5ft 10 ½ inches

2.

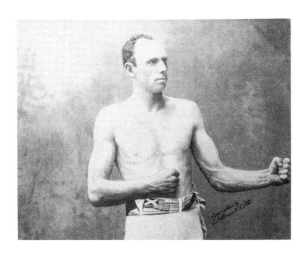

Born 26 May 1863
First British born boxer to win world Heavyweight title
Nick-name "Ruby Robert"

3.

Nick-name "The Galveston Giant"
Won world Heavyweight title in Australia in 1908
Lost world crown in Cuba in 1915

4.

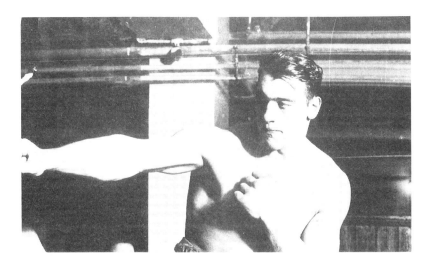

First Italian boxer to win world Heavyweight crown
Nick-name "The Ambling Alp"
Height 6ft 5¾ inches

5.

A: (Left)   Born 15 April 1939. Nationality: Welsh
   Won vacant WBC world Featherweight title in January 1968
B: (Right) Born 23 May 1954. Nationality: American
   Won world Middleweight Crown on 27 September 1980

6.　　　The boxer on the left of the photo:

Born 22 April 1960
Former British, European, Commonwealth and undisputed world
Welterweight champion
Won Commonwealth Light-Middleweight title in 1993

7.

A: (Left)　　Born 22 January 1964. Nationality: English
Height 5ft 9½ inches
B: (Right)　Born 16 November 1961. Nationality: English
Height 6ft 3½ inches

8.

Born on 7 December 1956. Nicknamed "The Body Snatcher"
Lost a twelve round points decision to James Toney in February
1997 for the vacant WBU Cruiserweight championship

9.

Born 8 August 1966
Former WBO Middleweight and Super Middleweight world title
holder
Knocked out Camilio Alarcon in round four on 27 March 1997

10.

Born on 30 August 1968. Nationality: Welsh
Won WBO version of the world Bantamweight title in April 1996

11.

Born 12 February 1974.
Won European Bantamweight tile in 1994.
Added the IBF version of the world Featherweight championship to his WBO crown by stopping Tom Johnson in eight rounds on 8 February 1997

12.

Won the vacant world WBO Heavyweight championship on 29 June 1996 by knocking out opponent Jeremy Williams
Made first defence of WBO title on 9 November 1996 against Alexander Zolkin stopping him in round ten
Made second defence of crown against fellow Briton Scott Welch on 11 January 1997 outpointing him over twelve rounds

13.

Born on 21 July 1964
Had first professional contest in America on 24 October 1986
Stopped Frederic Seillier in five rounds on 8 February 1997 in defence of his WBO world Super-Middleweight championship

14.

Born on 6 January 1964. Nationality: German
Lost IBF world Light-Heavyweight title when outpointed over
twelve rounds by WBA champion Virgil Hill in a unification match
which took place on 23 November 1996

15.

Born on 13 December 1968
Won vacant WBO world Featherweight title in 1993
Won vacant WBO Inter-Continental Featherweight title on 8 March
1997 by knocking out Tomas Santos Serrano in round one

16.

Nationality: American
Former IBF Middleweight and WBA Super-Middleweight world title holder
Stopped Challenger Rudy Nix on two rounds on 17 January 1997 in defence of his NABF Light-Heavyweight crown

17.

Born on 21 October 1968
Made professional debut on 12 November 1992
Won British Cruiserweight crown in 1995

18.

Born on 19 February 1971
Won the WBC world Super Middleweight title when knocking out
holder Vincenzo Nardiello in seven rounds on 12 October 1996
Made first defence of crown when stopping Giovanni Pretorius in
round seven on 8 February 1997

19.

A: (Left) Nationality : Scottish. Height 5ft 3 inches
       Lost in second bid for the vacant British flyweight title when
outpointed over twelve rounds by Adey Lewis on 27 January 1997
B: (Right): Nationality: English. Height 5ft 2½ inches
       Lost bid for world WBO Light-Flyweight crown when
outpointed by holder Baby Jake Matlala on 8 February 1997

20.

Born 23 March 1972
Won British Super-Middleweight crown in 1995
Knocked out Tyler Hughes in round one on 22 March 1997

21. (Left in photo)

Born 21 November 1969. Nationality: Puerto Rican
Former WBO Bantamweight and Super-Bantamweight world title
holder

22.

Boxes in southpaw stance. Nationality: Scottish
Stopped Jimmy Vincent in the first round on 25 March 1997

23.

Born 23 November 1967
First professional contest on 21 September 1989
Won European Super-Middleweight championship in 1995

24.

Born on 2 September 1965
Won European Heavyweight crown in 1990
Became first British born Heavyweight to regain the world title when stopping Oliver McCall in round five for the vacant WBC crown on 7 February 1997

25.

Strong associations with Frank Bruno (left of photo)
Former boxing commentator
"Boxing An Illustrated History" and "The Hardest Game" are just two of the books he has written on the sport

Photo Quiz Answers

1.   John L. Sullivan
2.   Bob Fitzsimmons
3.   Jack Johnson
4.   Primo Carnera
5.   **A.** Howard Winstone **B.** Marvin Hagler
6.   Lloyd Honeyghan
7.   **A.** Nigel Benn   **B.** Frank Bruno
8.   Mike McCallum
9.   Chris Eubank
10. Robbie Regan
11. Prince Naseem Hamed
12. Henry Akinwande
13. Steve Collins
14. Henry Maske
15. Steve Robinson
16. Michael Nunn
17. Terry Dunstan
18. Robin Reid
19   **A.** Keith Knox   **B.** Mickey Cantwell
20. Joe Calzaghe
21. Daniel Jimenez
22. Gary Jacobs
23. Henry Wharton
24. Lennox Lewis
25. Harry Carpenter

THE CHAMPIONSHIP QUIZ

ROUND ONE

1. Thomas Hearns won the WBA Welterweight title in 1980 when he stopped holder Pipino Cuevas in which round?
   A. One B. Two C. Three

2. Who was the first opponent to take Don Curry the full distance of ten rounds in the professional ranks?
   A. Vernon Lewis B. Eddie Campbell C. Curtis Ramsey

3. Who did Jimmy Cable defeat in 1984 to win the vacant British Light- Middleweight title with a twelve round points decision?
   A. Jimmy Batten B. Nick Wilshire C. Prince Rodney

4. During 1969 Paul Ferreri defeated Alan Presnell to win the vacant Australian Bantamweight title, by which method?
   A. Five round knockout B. Twelve round stoppage C. Fifteen round points decision

5. Chris Finnegan fought as a southpaw, *true or false*?

6. In which weight division was Miguel Cuello a WBC world title holder?
   A. Light-Middle B. Middle C. Light-Heavyweight

7. Matthew Saad Muhammad formerly boxed under which name?
   A. Matt Franklin B. Matt Johnson C. Matt Longman

8. Did Joe Louis ever defend his world Heavyweight title in England? *Yes or No*

9. Roberto Duran won the WBA version of the world Light-Middleweight title when he stopped holder Davey Moore in round Eight. where did this bout take place?
   A. New York B. Las Vegas C. Mexico City

10. Who did Vito Antuofermo defeat in 1979 with a fifteen round points decision to win the world Middleweight title?
   A. Hugo Corro B. Bennie Briscoe C. Rodrigo Valdes

11. In which weight division was Kim Ki-Soo a world champion?
   A. Welterweight B. Light-Middleweight
   C. Middleweight

12. Who was the last British fighter prior to Charlie Magri to hold a version of the world Flyweight title?
   A. Walter McGowan B. Terry Allen
   C. Jackie Paterson

13. Tony Sibson failed in his challenge for the world Middleweight title in 1983 when Marvin Hagler stopped him in which round?
   A. Five B. Six C. Seven

14. Who did Mike McCallum outpoint over fifteen rounds in 1984 to win the vacant WBA Light-Middleweight crown?
   A. Sean Mannion B. Tadashi Mihara C. Rocky Fratto

15. Where did the above contest take place?
   A. San Francisco B. New Orleans C. New York

16. During his career Australian Paul Ferreri once held the Commonwealth Featherweight title, *true or false?*

17. Former British Featherweight champion Jimmy Revie boxed in the southpaw stance, *true or false?*

18. Who did Barry McGuigan stop in two rounds when making his professional debut in 1981?
   A. Selvin Bell B. Gary Lucas C. Terry Pizzaro

19. Did Terry Marsh ever box in Mexico. *Yes or No?*

20. Patrizio Oliva of Italy won a medal in the 1980 Olympic Games. Was it **gold, silver** or **bronze**?

21. In 1982 Kelvin Smart won the vacant British Flyweight title when he knocked out Dave George in which round?
    A. Four B Five C. Six

22. David Pearce won the British Heavyweight title when he stopped which defending champion in nine rounds?
    A. Gordon Ferris B. John L. Gardner C. Neville Meade

23. During 1982 Juan Laporte won the vacant WBC Featherweight title when opponent Mario Miranda retired in which round?
    A. Nine B. Ten C. Eleven

24. Where did the above contest take place?
    A. New York B. San Juan C. Atlantic City

25. In 1982 Hector Camacho defended the NABF Super-Featherweight title against Refugio Rojas and stopped him in which round?
    A. One B. Two C. Three

26. Marvin Johnson stopped Mate Parlov in ten rounds during 1978 to win the WBC Light-Heavyweight title. In which country did this contest take place?
    A. Italy B. Germany C. America

27. How many times did Henry Cooper contest the world Heavyweight title?
    A. Once B. Twice C. Three times

28. During his professional career which British title did Dave Needham **not** hold?
    A. Bantamweight B. Featherweight
    C. Super-Featherweight

29. In defence of his WBA Bantamweight title in 1976 Alfonso Zamora knocked out a future WBA Featherweight champion in two rounds. Who was it?
    A. Eusebio Pedroza B. Rafael Ortega C. Cecilio Lastra

30. Who did Aaron Pryor knock out in four rounds during 1980 to win the WBA Light-Welterweight title?
    A. Saoul Mamby B. Antonio Cervantes C. Leroy Haley

31. During 1982 a British boxer outpointed Roberto Duran over ten rounds in Detroit. Name him.
    A. Jimmy Batten B. Prince Rodney C. Kirkland Laing

32. How many times did Ken Buchanan and Ismael Laguna meet in contests for the world Lightweight title?
    A. Once B. Twice C. Three times

33. Did former European & British Middleweight champion Kevin Finnegan ever contest a world title? *Yes or No*

34. Which version of the world Light-Middleweight title did Elisha Obed hold?
    A. WBA B. IBF C. WBC

35. Who did Frank Cedeno stop in round six during 1983 to become the WBC Flyweight champion?
    A. Freddie Castillo B. Eleoncio Mercedes
    C. Charlie Magri

36. How many times did Joe Bugner challenge for the world Heavyweight title during 1975-6?
    A. Once B. Twice C. Three times

37. In 1979 Clinton McKenzie was outpointed over ten rounds in Las Vegas by a future world WBC Light-Welterweight champion. Name him.
    A. Leroy Haley B. Bruce Curry C. Saoul Mamby

38. Which title did Clinton McKenzie **not** hold during his career at Light-Welterweight?
    A. European B. British C. Commonwealth

39. During March of 1983 Milton McCrory of America met Colin Jones of Wales in Reno for the vacant WBC Welterweight title. What was the result?
A. A points victory for Jones B. A points victory for McCrory C. A twelve round draw

40. During his career which World Middleweight champion did Kevin Finnegan not box?
A. Marvin Hagler B. Alan Minter C. Vito Autuofermo

41. In which weight division was Gratien Tonna of France a European champion?
A. Light-Middleweight B. Middleweight C. Light-Heavyweight

42. Did Bunny Sterling ever challenge for the World Middleweight title, *yes or no*?

43. How many times did Dave "Boy" Green challenge for the WBC Welterweight title?
A. Once B. Twice C. Three times

44. In which weight division was Miguel De Oliveira a WBC world champion?
A. Welterweight B. Light-Middleweight C. Middleweight

45. Who did Jose Legra stop in five rounds in 1968 to win the WBC Featherweight title?.
A. Howard Winstone B. Clemente Sanchez C. Eder Jofre

46. Did Ken Buchanan ever contest a world title in Scotland?
Yes or no

47. In which weight division was Raul Rojas a WBA champion?
A. Bantamweight B. Featherweight C. Lightweight

48. Who did Richard Dunn stop in three rounds in 1976 to win the vacant European heavyweight title?.
A. Bernd August B. Dante Cane C. Jean-Pierre Coopman

49. ***True or false,*** Richard Dunn boxed in the southpaw stance?

50. How many times did John H. Stracey and Dave "Boy" Green meet in the professional ranks?
A. Once B. Twice C. Three times

51. Who did Lottie Mwale stop in five rounds during 1979 to win the Commonwealth Light-Heavyweight title?
A. Tony Mundine B. Gary Summerhays C. Steve Aczel

52. Who did Lloyd Honeyghan outpoint over twelve rounds in 1983 to win the vacant British Welterweight title?
A. Cliff Gilpin B. Peter Neal C. Kirkland Laing

53. In 1970 John McCluskey won the vacant commonwealth Flyweight crown when he outpointed Harry Hayes over fifteen rounds. Where did the contest take place?
A. Scotland B. Zambia C. Australia

54. Which round did Milton McCrory stop Milton Guest in defence of his WBC Welterweight crown in 1984?
A. Five B. Six C. Seven

55. To defend the WBC Light-Middleweight title in 1984 in which round did Thomas Hearns knock out Roberto Duran?
A. One B. Two C. Three

56. Where did the above contest take place?
A. Las Vegas B. Atlantic City C. Detroit

57. In which weight division was Piet Crous a WBA world title holder?
A. Light-Heavy B. Cruiserweight C. Heavyweight

58. From which country did Piet Crous originate?
A. Australia B. New Zealand C. South Africa

59. In 1984 who did Germany's Georg Steinherr outpoint over 12 rounds to win the European Light-Middleweight title?
A. Jimmy Cable B. Said Skouma C. Germain LeMaitre

60. Did former European, British and Commonwealth Middleweight champion Tony Sibson box in the southpaw stance? *Yes or No*

61. Which boxer was **not** from Brockton, Mass in America?
    A. Marvin Hagler B. Rocky Marciano C. Gene Hatcher

62. In which weight division was Dave "Boy" Green **not** a European title holder?
    A. Light-Welterweight B. Welterweight
    C. Light-Middleweight

63. During 1984 Larry Holmes made just one defence of the IBF Heavyweight title stopping his challenger in round twelve. Who was it against?
    A. James "Bonecrusher" Smith B. Tim Witherspoon
    C. Scott Frank

64. In which weight division was Marvin Camel a WBC world title holder?
    A. Middle B. Light-heavy C. Cruiser

65. Who did Johnny Bumphus outpoint over fifteen rounds in 1984 to win the vacant WBA Light-Welterweight crown?
    A. Leroy Haley B. Saoul Mamby C. Lorenzo Garcia

66. Which of these boxers has the Christian name of Floyd?
    A. Patterson B. Havard C. Conteh

67. Who was the first man to take Frank Bruno the full distance of ten rounds in the professional ranks?
    A. Phil Brown B. Jeff Jordan C. Ken Lakusta

68. To win the European Heavyweight Championship Steffen Tangstad outpointed Lucien Rodriguez over twelve rounds in 1984. In which country did the contest take place?
    A. France B. Italy C. Denmark

69. In Atlantic City during 1983 Tony Sibson stopped opponent John Collins in which round?
    A. One B. Two C. Three

70. In 1984 Azumah Nelson stopped Wilfredo Gomez in round 11 to win which version of the world Featherweight title?
    A. WBA B. IBF C. WBC

71. *True or false,* Chris and Kevin Finnegan are brothers?

72. Did former British Lightweight champion Maurice Cullen ever challenge for a world title during his career? *Yes or No*

73. In 1984 John Feeney fought for the vacant European Bantamweight title and was outpointed over twelve rounds by which opponent?
    A. Ciro De Leva B. Walter Giorgetti
    C. Giuseppe Fossati

74. In 1983 the then British Lightweight Champion George Feeney was outpointed over ten rounds by the WBA Champion Ray Mancini. Where did the bout take place?
    A. America B. England C. Italy

75. *True or false* George and John Feeney are brothers?

76. Terry Marsh won the British Light-Welterweight title in 1984 by defeating Clinton McKenzie by which method?
    A. Five round stoppage B. Eight round knockout
    C. Twelve round points decision

77. On 6 December 1983 Lloyd Honeyghan made the first defence of his British Welterweight crown and outpointed which challenger over twelve rounds?
    A. Sid Smith B. Cliff Gilpin C. Kostas Petrou

78. During his career which Welterweight title did Ralph Charles not hold?
    A. British B. European C. World

79. In 1981 Pinklon Thomas knocked out Lee Mitchell in which round?
A. One B. Two C. Three

80. How many bouts did Carlos de Leon have in 1981?
A. One B. Two C. Three

81. During his professional career which Flyweight title did John McCluskey not hold?
A. British B. Commonwealth C. World

82. From which part of America did Don Curry originate?
A. Detroit B. Kentucky C. Texas

83. Mike McCallum took part in how many contests in 1982?
A. Six B. Seven C. Eight

84. During his professional career Alan Rudkin failed to win the World Bantamweight title. How many times did he challenge for the crown?
A. Once B. Twice C. Three times

85. Did Barry McGuigan and Pat Cowdell ever box in the professional ranks? *Yes or No*

86. George Feeney challenged Rene Weller for the European Lightweight title in 1984 but was outpointed over twelve rounds. In which country did the bout take place?
A. Italy B. England C. Germany

87. During 1979 Marvin Hagler challenged Vito Antuofermo for the world Middleweight crown. What was the result?
A. Win for Hagler B. A win for Antuofermo C. A draw

88. Who did Julio Cesar Chavez knock out in six rounds on 5 September 1980?
A. Miguel Cebrero B. Andres Felix C. Fidel Navarro

89. Livingstone Bramble was a WBA Champion in which weight division?
   A. Lightweight B. Welterweight C. Middleweight

90. During his career how many times did Carlos Monzon defend his world Middleweight title?
   A. Ten times B. Twelve times C. Fourteen times

91. Who was the first holder of the commonwealth Cruiserweight title?
   A. Steve Aczel B. Chisanda Mutti C. Stewart Lithgo

92. Which version of the world Light-Welterweight title did Terry Marsh hold?
   A. WBC B. WBA C. IBF

93. Who did Herol Graham knockout in two rounds in 1983 to win the vacant European-Light Middleweight crown?
   A. Clemente Tshinza B. Said Skouma C. Claude Martin

94. To regain the European Middleweight title in 1984 Tony Sibson outpointed Louis Acaries over twelve rounds. Where did the contest take place?
   A. England B. Italy C. France

95. During his pro-career did Mark Kaylor ever challenge for the World Middleweight crown? *Yes or No*

96. During his career Joe Bugner boxed twice in Mexico, *true or false?*

97. In 1983 Juan Laporte defended his WBC Featherweight crown against Johnny De La Rosa and defeated him by which method?
   A. Two round stoppage B. Eight round knockout
   C. Twelve round points decision

98. In 1983 Tyrone Rackley fought Bruce Curry and was stopped in which round?
   A. One B. Two C. Three

ROUND TWO

99. Where did the above contest take place?
    A. Reno B. Las Vegas C. Fort Worth

100. How many bouts did Gerrie Coetzee have in 1979?
    A. One B. Two C. Three

101. In the Olympic Games of 1980 a medal was won by Tony Willis. Which colour was it?
    A. Gold B. Silver C. Bronze

102. Frank Bruno made his professional debut in America during 1983, knocking out opponent Mike Jameson in two rounds. Where did the contest take place?
    A. Las Vegas B. San Francisco C. Chicago

103. In which weight division was Roy Smith a British champion?
    A. Super-Middleweight B. Light-Heavyweight
    C. Cruiserweight

104. Johnny Nelson made his professional debut on 18 March 1986 matched against Peter Brown in a six round contest .What was the result?
    A. Points win for Brown B. Points win for Nelson
    C. A draw

105. Who did Gary Mason knockout in four rounds to win the vacant British Heavyweight title?
    A. Hughroy Currie B. Jess Harding C. Glen McCrory

106. In defence of his WBA Flyweight crown in 1988 Fidel Bassa outpointed Dave "Boy" McAuley over twelve rounds. Where did the contest take place?
    A. England B. Ireland C. Scotland

71

107. Who was the first holder of the European Cruiserweight title?
    A. Angelo Rottoli *B. Magne Havnaa* *C. Sam Reeson*

108. How many European Heavyweight title bouts did Joe Bugner participate in during his professional career?
    A. Seven *B. Eight* *C. Nine*

109. How many contests did Paul Hodkinson have in 1988?
    A. One *B. Two* *C. Three*

110. Orlando Canizales defended his IBF Bantamweight title against Billy Hardy in 1990 and won a twelve round points decision. Where did the contest take place?
    A. Sunderland *B. Wembley* *C. Stockton*

111. In which weight division was Joey Jacobs British Champion?
    A. Super-Featherweight *B. Featherweight* *C. Lightweight*

112. On 6 October 1987 Dennis Andries outpointed Robert Folley over ten rounds in Phoenix America. *True or false:* Robert is the son of former world Heavyweight contender Zora Folley?

113. In which year did Mike Tyson make his professional debut?
    A. 1984 *B. 1985* *C. 1986*

114. During 1986 Duke McKenzie outpointed Piero Pinna over twelve rounds in defence of his European Flyweight title. Where did the contest take place?
    A. Italy *B. England* *C. France*

115. In a contest for the vacant WBC Cruiserweight title Carlos de Leon stopped Britain's Sam Reeson in which round?
    A. Seven *B. Eight* *C. Nine*

116. In which year did the above contest take place?
    A. 1988 *B. 1989* *C. 1990*

117. To win the British Light-Middleweight title Gary Stretch defeated Gary Cooper by which method?
A. Five round knockout B. Eight round stoppage
C. Twelve round points decision

118. In 1986 Mike Tyson stopped Dave Jaco in which round?
A. One B. Two C. Three

119. During 1989 Frank Bruno attempted to take the world Heavyweight title from Mike Tyson, but failed when stopped in which round?
A. Three B. Four C. Five

120. In which country did the above contest take place?
A. England B. America C. France

121. To win the vacant British Light-Welterweight title Pat Barrett knocked out Tony Willis in which round?
A. Nine B. Ten C. Eleven

122. In which round did Marlon Starling stop Lloyd Honeyghan to win the WBC Welterweight title?
A. Eight B. Nine C. Ten

123. In which American city did the contest take place?
A. Las Vegas B. San Francisco C. Boston

124. To win the vacant European Light-Middleweight crown in 1986 Chris Pyatt stopped John Van Elteren in which round?
A. One B. Two C. Three

125. During 1989 Jim McDonnell stopped Barry McGuigan in which round?
A. Two B. Three C. Four

126. Where did the above contest take place?
A. England B. Ireland C. Scotland

127. How many bouts did Nigel Benn have in 1988?
A. Seven B. Eight C. Nine

128. Which Commonwealth title did Michael Watson hold?
A. Middleweight B. Super-Middleweight
C. Light-Heavyweight

129. Did Joe Bugner box George Foreman in 1987-8? *Yes or No*

130. Mark Kaylor once challenged for the British Light-Heavyweight crown, *true or false?*

131. In which year did Gary Jacobs make his professional debut?
A. 1984 B. 1985 C. 1986

132. In his career, how many professional contests did Frankie Jones, the former British & Empire Flyweight Champion have?
A. 23 B. 24 C. 25

133. During 1989 Del Bryan outpointed Javier Castillejos over eight rounds. In which country did this contest take place?
A. England B. France C. Spain

134. On 15 August 1989 Ray Mercer knocked out Tracy Thomas in which round?
A. One B. Two C. Three

135. Lloyd Honeyghan outpointed Delfino Marin over ten rounds in 1989. Where did the contest take place?
A. America B. England C. Scotland

136. To win the vacant Australian Junior Welterweight crown on 16 August 1989 Tony Jones stopped Pat Leglise in which round?
A. Eight B. Nine C. Ten

137. On 3 September 1989 Roy Jones stopped Ron Amundsen in which round?
A. Five B. Six C. Seven

138. In which year did Ross Hale make his professional debut?
    A. 1989 B. 1990 C. 1991

139. Tony Morrison won the vacant Canadian Heavyweight crown in 1989 by defeating Ken Lakusta by which method?
    A. Stopped in two B. Knockout in six
    C. Outpointed over twelve rounds

140. When did Drew Docherty make his professional start?
    A. 1987 B. 1988 C. 1989

141. In a contest for the Commonwealth Super-Featherweight title Mark Reefer outpointed John Sichula over twelve rounds. Who was the referee of this bout?
    A. Adrian Morgan B. Larry O'Connell C. John Coyle

142. Colin McMillan outpointed Graham O'Malley during 1989 over how many rounds?
    A. Six B. Eight C. Ten

143. To win the vacant British Super-Middleweight crown Sam Storey defeated Tony Burke by which method?
    A. Stoppage in round one B. Knockout in round eight
    C. Twelve round point decision

144. Who was the referee of the above contest?
    A. John Coyle B. Adrian Morgan C. Larry O' Connell

145. To win the vacant WBA Inter-Continental Welterweight title Glenwood Brown stopped Donovan Boucher in which round?
    A. Seven B. Eight C. Nine

146. In which round did Riddick Bowe stop Mick Acey on 19 October 1989?
    A. One B. Two C. Three

147. Who was the first man to take Nigel Benn the full distance of ten rounds in the professional ranks?
A. Sanderline Williams B. Jorge Amparo
C. Lenzie Morgan

148. In defence of his WBC Super-Featherweight crown Azumah Nelson stopped challenger Jim McDonnell in which round?
A. Eight B. Ten C. Twelve

149. Who was the referee of the above contest?
A. Richard Steele B. Joe Cortez C. Mills Lane

150. In which country did the above contest take place?
A. England B. America C. France

151. Was Azumah Nelson the first man to stop Jim McDonnell in the pro ranks? *Yes or No*

152. When did Henry Akinwande make his professional debut?
A. 1989 B. 1990 C. 1991

153. In which round did Mike Dokes stop Lionel Washington to win the vacant WBA Intercontinental and Calfornia State titles?
A. Six B. Seven C. Eight

154. Who was the referee of the above contest?
A. Larry Rozadilla B. Mills Lane C. Richard Steele

155. During 1989 Tommy Morrison outpointed Lorenzo Candy over how many rounds?
A. Six B. Eight C. Ten

156. In which round did Pat Barrett stop Joey Ferrell in 1989?
A. Six B. Seven C. Eight

157. In which year did Glenn McCrory win the IBF vacant Cruiserweight title?
A. 1989 B. 1990 C. 1991

158. Which opponent did he defeat to win the crown?
  A. Siza Makhathini B. Patrick Lumumba C. Jeff Lampkin

159. By which method did he win?
  A. A five round stoppage B. Eight round knockout
  C. Twelve round points decision

160. Was Glenn McCrory the first British boxer to win a version of the world Cruiserweight title? *Yes or No*

161. In which country did the above contest take place?
  A. America B. Italy C. England

162. In which year did Herbie Hide make his first professional appearance?
  A. 1987 B. 1988. C. 1989

163. *True or false,* former WBA world Heavyweight Champion Mike Dokes boxed in the southpaw stance?

164. On 28 November 1989 Robert Daniels won the vacant WBA Cruiserweight title when he defeated Dwight Muhammad Qawi by which method?
  A. Knockout in round eight B. Stopped in round ten
  C. Twelve round points decision

165. In defence of the British Super-Middleweight title Sam Storey stopped Noel Magee in which round?
  A. Nine B. Ten C. Eleven

166. Who was the referee of the above contest?
  A. Dave Parris B. Larry O' Connell C. John Coyle

167. During 1989 Victor Cordova outpointed Jose Da Silva over how many rounds?
  A. Six B. Eight C. Ten

168. How did John Lowey defeat Ariel Cordova on 29 November 1989?
    A. Knockout in round three B. Stopped in round four
    C. Outpointed over six rounds

169. *True or false* Tony Swift stopped Seamus O'Sullivan in the first round in their 1989 encounter?

170. To win the Cruiserweight Commonwealth title Derek Angol defeated Apollo Sweet by which method?
    A. Knockout in round four B. Stoppage in round eight
    C. Twelve round points decision

171. Where was the above contest held?
    A. Australia B. England C. New Zealand

172. In which country did Chris Eubank start his professional career?
    A. England B. America C. France

173. In which round did Bobby Czyz knockout Horacio Brandan during 1990?
    A. Six B. Seven C. Eight

174. .On the 25th September 1990 George Foreman knocked out Terry Anderson in which round?
    A. One B. Two C. Three

175. In which country did the above contest take place?
    A. America B. Italy C. England

176. Thierry Jacob won the vacant European Bantamweight title when he defeated Duke McKenzie by which method?
    A. Six round stoppage B. Nine round knockout
    C. Twelve round points decision

177. In which country did the above contest take place?
    A. England B. France C. Italy

178. In which round did Frank Tate stop Greg Everett in 1990?
A. Five B. Six C. Seven

179. The contest between Tracy Harris Patterson and Julio Blanco took place on 27 September 1990. What was the result?
A. Ten round points victory for Blanco B. Five round stoppage for Patterson C. A ten round draw

180. How did Milton McCrory defeat Mike Sacchetti in 1990?
A. Four round stoppage B. Six round knockout
C. Ten round points decision

181. In defence of his IBF Middleweight crown Michael Nunn stopped Don Curry in which round?
A. Eight B. Nine C. Ten

182. In their contest Gary Mason defeated opponent Everett "Big Foot" Martin by which method?
A. Eight round stoppage B. Nine round knockout
C. Ten round points decision

183. In the above contest was Mason at any time down for a count? *Yes or No*

184. To win the world Heavyweight title James "Buster" Douglas knocked out Mike Tyson in which round?
A. Ten B. Eleven C. Twelve

185. Who was the referee of the above contest?
A. Mills Lane B. Richard Steele C. Octavio Meyran

186. In which country did the contest take place?
A. America B. Japan C. Mexico

187. In defence of his WBC Light-Heavyweight crown Jeff Harding stopped Nestor Giovannini in which round?
A. Nine B. Ten C. Eleven

188. Brian Mitchell defeated Jackie Beard in defence of his WBA Super-Featherweight title in 1980 by which method?
A. Eight round stoppage B. Ten round knockout C. Twelve round points decision

189. ***True or false*** Brian Mitchell once held the WBC Featherweight crown?

190. In defence of his British Cruiserweight title Johnny Nelson stopped Lou Gent in which round?
A. Two B. Three C. Four

191. Who was the referee of the above contest?
A. Adrian Morgan B. Dave Parris C. Wynford Jones

192. ***True or false,*** Johnny Nelson was the first British Cruiserweight champion in the history of the division to win a Lonsdale Belt outright?

193. Nate "Mr" Miller retained his NABF Cruiserweight crown when he defeated Tyrone Booze by which method?
A. Ten round stoppage B. Eleven round knockout C. Twelve round points decision

194. Mike "The Bounty" Hunter won the vacant WBA Intercontinental Cruiserweight title when he defeated Dwight Muhammad Qawi by which method?
A. Two round stoppage B. Five round knockout C. Twelve round points decision

195. To win the WBC Light-Middleweight crown Terry Norris knocked out John Mugabi in which round?
A. One B. Two C. Three

196. ***True or false*** in a previous contest Mugabi had defeated Norris?

197. In defence of the WBA Middleweight title Mike McCallum knocked out Michael Watson in which round?
A. Nine B. Ten C. Eleven

ROUND THREE

198. Who was the referee of the above contest?
     A. Mills Lane B. Richard Steele C. Roberto Ramirez

199. In which country did the contest take place?
     A. England B. America C. France

200. In which round did Lennox Lewis knockout opponent Mike Simwelu on 14 April 1990?
     A. One B. Two C. Three

201. In defence of his IBF Middleweight crown Michael Nunn outpointed a former world Welterweight champion on 14 April 1990. Who was he?
     A. Lloyd Honeyghan B. Marlon Starling
     C. Jorge Vaca

202. To win the WBO version of the world Middleweight crown on 29 April 1990 Nigel Benn stopped Doug de Witt in which round?
     A. Eight B. Nine C. Ten

203. Who was the referee of the above contest?
     A. Roberto Ramirez B. Randy Neumann C. Mills Lane

204. In which American city did the contest take place?
     A. Las Vegas B. San Francisco C. Atlantic City

205. In defence of his WBO Light Heavyweight crown Michael Moorer knocked out Mario Melo in which round?
     A. One B. Two C. Three

206. In defence of his WBC and IBF Lightweight titles Pernell Whitaker defeated challenger Azumah Nelson by which method?
     A. Eight round stoppage B. Ten round knockout
     C. Twelve round points decision

207. To win the vacant British Featherweight championship Sean Murphy knocked out John Doherty in which round?
A. One B. Two C. Three

208. Sean Murphy was a previous holder of the British Bantamweight title, *true or false?*

209. What was the result of the Nicky Piper vs Maurice Core contest which took place in 1990?
A. Six round points victory for Piper B. Six round points victory for Core C. Six round draw

210. To win the vacant WBC international Light-Middleweight title Tony Collins defeated opponent Hugo Marinangeli by which method?
A. Six round stoppage B. Nine round knockout
C. Twelve round points decision

211. In which round did Marcos Villasana stop Paul Hodkinson to win the vacant WBC Featherweight title?
A. Eight B. Nine C. Ten

212. To win the vacant IBC Super-Bantamweight crown Jesus Salud stopped Martin Ortegon in which round?
A. Nine B. Ten C. Eleven

213. In 1990 how did Julian Jackson defeat Wayne Powell?
A. Stopped in round two B. Knock out in round four
C. Ten round points decision

214. Which European title did Herol Graham **not** hold during his career?
A. Light-Middle B. Middle C. Light-Heavy

215. In which round did Johnny Nelson stop Arthur Weathers in their 1990 contest?
A. One B. Two C. Three

216. By which method did Herbie Hide defeat Alek Penarski during 1990?
    A. Stopped in round three B. Knockout in round eight C. Ten round points decision

217. *True or false*, the above contest took place at the Albert Hall?

218. To win the vacant European Cruiserweight title Johnny Nelson stopped Markus Bott in which round?
    A. Ten B. Eleven C. Twelve

219. How many contests did Nicky Piper have in 1990?
    A. Two B. Three C. Four

220. To win the vacant NABF Light-Middleweight crown Brett Lally stopped Robert Hines in which round?
    A. Two B. Three C. Four

221. *Yes or No* Welshman Carl Gizzi once held the British Heavyweight crown?

222. To regain the WBC Light-Heavyweight crown Dennis Andries knocked out Jeff Harding in which round on 28 July 1990?
    A. Six B. Seven C. Eight

223. In which country did the above contest take place?
    A. England B. France C. Australia

224. *True or false*, Dennis Andries became the first British fighter to win the same world crown three times?

225. To win the vacant European Flyweight crown Pat Clinton defeated Salvatore Fanni by which method?
    A. Ten round stoppage B. Eleven round knockout C. Twelve round points decision

226. In which country did the above contest take place?
    A. Scotland B. England C. Italy

227. To retain his WBC and IBF versions of the world Lightweight titles and also win the WBA crown Pernell Whitaker knocked out Juan Nazario in which round? (Note: Nazario was defending WBA Championship)
   A. One B. Two C. Three

228. In defence of his WBO middleweight crown Nigel Benn stopped challenger Iran Barkley in which round?
   A. One B. Four C. Six

229. In which country did the above contest take place?
   A. America B. England C. France

230. In which round did Steve Collins stop Fermin Chirino in 1990?
   A. Four B. Five C. Six

231. When did Robbie Regan make his professional debut?
   A. 1988 B. 1989 C. 1990

232. Johnny Armour outpointed Lupe Castro over how many rounds in 1990?
   A. Six B. Eight C. Ten

233. To win the vacant British Light-Heavyweight crown in 1990 who did Steve McCarthy outpoint over Twelve rounds?
   A. Tom Collins B. Serg Fame C. Crawford Ashley

234. When did Crawford Ashley make his professional debut?
   A. 1987 B. 1988 C. 1989

235. Who was the first man to defeat Pat Clinton in the professional ranks?
   A. Eyup Can B. Danny Porter C. David Afan-Jones

236. How many professional bouts did Chris Eubank have in 1988?
   A. Three B. Four C. Five

237. To win the world Heavyweight title Evander Holyfield knocked out James "Buster" Douglas in which round?
A. One B. Two C. Three

238. To win the British Super-Middleweight crown James Cook stopped Sam Storey in which round?
A. Eight B. Nine C. Ten

239. Where did the above contest take place?
A. Battersea B. Belfast C. Southwark

240. In a previous bid for a British title in 1988, James Cook was stopped in round five by Herol Graham for which vacant crown?
A. Light-Middle B. Middle C. Light-Heavy

241. In which round did Nicky Piper knockout John Ellis in their 1990 encounter?
A. One B. Two C. Three

242. Tommy Morrison stopped Mike Acey in round one during 1990, *true or false?*

243. *Yes or No,* Tommy Morrison boxed in England in 1991?

244. In which round did Antonio Rivera knockout Giovanni Parisi during 1990?
A. Two B. Three C. Four

245. To win the WBO version of the world Middleweight title Chris Eubank stopped Nigel Benn in which round?
A. Nine B. Ten C. Eleven

246. To retain his WBC Light-Welterweight crown Julio Cesar Chavez defeated challenger Lonnie Smith by which method?
A. Four round stoppage B. Eight round knockout
C. Twelve round points decision

247. From which country did former world Flyweight champion Sot Chitalada originate?
A. *Japan* B. *Thailand* C. *Korea*

248. On 12 February 1991 Robbie Regain defeated Kevin Jenkins for the vacant Welsh Flyweight title by which method?
A. *Four round stoppage* B. *Eight round knockout*
C. *Ten round points decision*

249. Where did the above contest take place?
A. *Llanelli* B. *Cardiff* C. *Merthyr*

250. At that moment in time Robbie Regan was undefeated in how many bouts?
A. *Seven* B. *Eight* C. *Ten*

251. During 1991 Larry Holmes defeated Eddie Gonzales by which method?
A. *One round knockout* B. *Eight round points decision*
C. *Ten round points decision*

252. *True or false* Larry Holmes boxed in Britain during 1990?

253. *True or false* prior to winning the world Heavyweight title Evander Holyfield was the first undisputed holder of the world Cruiserweight championship?

254. In which round did Richie Woodhall stop Nigel Moore in their 1991 encounter?
A. *One* B. *Two* C. *Three*

255. In which round did Neville Brown stop Paul Smith in their 1991 meeting?
A. *One* B. *Two* C. *Three*

256. In defence of his IBF Flyweight crown Dave McAuley knocked out Baby Jake Matlala in which round?
A. *Ten* B. *Eleven* C. *Twelve*

257. To win the vacant IBF Cruiserweight title James Warring knocked out James Pritchard in which round?
   A. One B. Two C. Three

258. In which year did Terry Norris defend his WBC Light-Middleweight crown against Jorge Castro?
   A. 1990 B. 1991 C. 1992

259. In defence of his WBA Super-Middleweight title Victor Cordoba stopped Vincenzo Nardiello in which round?
   A. Ten B. Eleven C. Twelve

260. During his career did Walter McGowan ever hold a European title? *Yes or No*

261. In which round did Pat Barrett stop Mike Johnson in their 1991 contest?
   A. One B. Two C. Three

262. *True or false* Barrett was down for two counts in the first round in the above contest?

263. During 1992 which former world Welterweight king did Roy Jones knockout in round one?
   A. Lloyd Honeyghan B. Marlon Starling
   C. Jorge Vaca

264. During 1991 Robbie Regan won the vacant British Flyweight crown when he defeated Joe Kelly by which method?
   A. Three round knockout B. Eight round stoppage
   C. Twelve round points decision

265. Where did the above contest take place?
   A. Scotland B. England C. South Wales

266. What nickname did former world Heavyweight champion Joe Frazier have?
   A. The destroyer B. Smokin Joe C. Joe the puncher

267. To win the vacant WBO Super-Middleweight crown Chris Eubank stopped Michael Watson in which round?
A. Ten B. Eleven C. Twelve

268. Where did the above contest take place?
A. Tottenham B. Brighton C. Manchester

269. To win the WBC Featherweight crown Paul Hodkinson defeated holder Marcos Villasana by which method?
A. Eight round stoppage B. Eleven round knockout C. Twelve round points decision

270. To win the WBO world Bantamweight title Duke McKenzie defeated defending champion Gaby Canizales by which method?
A. Four round stoppage B. Eight round knockout C. Twelve round points decision

271. In which country did the above contest take place?
A. England B. America C. Mexico

272. Colin McMillan outpointed Percy Commey over twelve rounds to win the vacant Commonwealth Featherweight crown. In which year did the contest take place?
A. 1990 B. 1991 C. 1992

273. Meldrick Taylor defeated Glenwood Brown in defence of his WBA Welterweight crown by which method?
A. Ten round stoppage B. Eleven round knockout C. Twelve round points decision

274. *True or false* Meldrick Taylor outpointed Lloyd Honeyghan in 1991?

275. In which Rocky film did former world Heavyweight champion Joe Frazier appear?
A. One B. Two C. Three

276. How did Henry Wharton defeat opponent Nicky Walker on 23 January 1992?
A. Four round stoppage B. Eight round knockout
C. Ten round points decision

277. To win the British Flyweight crown in 1991 Francis Ampofo defeated Robbie Regan by which method?
A. Eight round knockout B. Eleven round stoppage
C. Twelve round points decision

278. This was Robbie Regan's first professional defeat, *true or false?*

279. *True or false* Robbie Regan had previously defeated Francis Ampofo on points over six rounds in just his second professional contest?

280. In a return contest on 17 December 1991 Robbie Regan regained the British Flyweight crown when he defeated Francis Ampofo by which method?
A. Stopped in three B. Knockout in six
C. Twelve round points decision

281. To win the vacant British Bantamweight title Joe Kelly defeated Ronnie Carroll by which method?
A. One round stoppage B. Three round knockout
C. Twelve round points decision

282. Where did the above contest take place?
A. Glasgow B. London C. Cardiff

283. In defence of his WBC Light-Flyweight title Humberto Gonzalez defeated Domingo Sosa by which method?
A. Two round stoppage B. Six round knockout
C. Twelve round points decision

284. In which round did Willie Beattie stop Gordon Blair to win the vacant Scottish Welterweight crown in 1992?
A. One B. Two C. Three

285. By which method did Lennox Lewis defeat opponent Levi Billups on 1 February 1992?
A. *Two round stoppage* B. *Three round knockout*
C. *Ten round points decision*

286. Where did the above contest take place?.
A. *Canada* B. *England* C. *America*

287. Over how many rounds did Larry Holmes outpoint Ray Mercer on 7 February 1992?
A. *Eight* B. *Ten* C. *Twelve*

288. *Yes or no*, Ray Mercer had been the WBO Heavyweight champion prior to the Holmes bout, but relinquished the title?

289. In defence of his IBF Middleweight title James Toney defeated challenger Dave Tiberi by which method?
A. *Three round stoppage* B. *Five round knockout*
C. *Twelve round points decision*

290. Tony Pep won the Commonwealth Super-Featherweight crown when he defeated champion Paul Harvey by which method?
A. *Four round stoppage* B. *Six round knockout*
C. *Twelve round points decision*

291. In which country did the above contest take place?
A. *Canada* B. *England* C. *Australia*

292. In which round did Tommy Morrison stop Bobby Quarry in 1992?
A. *One* B. *Two* C. *Three*

293. *True or false* Bobby is the brother of former Heavyweight contender Jerry Quarry?

294. What was the result when Danny Porter challenged Salvatore Fanni for the European Flyweight crown on 12 February 1992?
   A. Twelve round draw B. Points win for Porter
   C. Points win for Fanni

295. How did Sumbu Kalambay defeat Herol Graham to win the European Middleweight title on 26 May 1987?
   A. Five round stoppage B. Six round knockout
   C. Twelve round points decision

296. Where did the above contest take place?
   A. Italy B. England C. France

297. To win the WBO version of the world Flyweight title Pat Clinton defeated Isidro Perez by which method?
   A. Eight round stoppage B. Six round knockout
   C. Twelve round points decision

298. Where did the above contest take place?
   A. Scotland B. Mexico C. America

299. **True or false** former WBA world Heavyweight king Tony Tubbs boxed in the southpaw stance?

300. In defence of his IBF Light-Flyweight title Michael Carbajal defeated challenger Marcos Pacheco by which method?
   A. Nine round stoppage B. Eleven round knockout
   C. Twelve round points decision

301. In which round did Roy Jones knockout Art Serwando on 3 April 1992?
   A. One B. Four C. Six

302. In which round in 1992 did Riddick Bowe knock out Conroy Nelson?
   A. One B. Two C. Three

303. When did Eamonn Loughran make his professional debut?
   A. 1986 B. 1987 C. 1988

ROUND FOUR

304. In defence of his WBC Featherweight crown Paul Hodkinson stopped Steve Cruz in which round?
    A. One B. Two C. Three

305. In which country did the above contest take place?
    A. Mexico B. America C. Ireland

306. Which version of the world Featherweight title did Cruz once hold?
    A. WBC B. IBF C. WBA

307. To win the vacant Commonwealth Bantamweight title Johnny Armour defeated Ndaba Dube by which method?
    A. Stopped in Eight B. Stopped in twelve
    C. Twelve round points decision

308. In which country did the above contest take place?
    A. England B. Australia C. Scotland

309. At this stage of his career Johnny Armour was undefeated in how many contests?
    A. Six B. Seven C. Eight

310. To win the WBO world Featherweight crown Colin McMillan defeated Maurizio Stecca by which method?
    A. Five round stoppage B. Eight round knockout
    C. Twelve round points decision

311. Where did the above contest take place?
    A. England B. Italy C. Spain

312. In defence of his WBC Light-Middleweight crown Terry Norris stopped Meldrick Taylor in which round?
    A. Four B. Five C. Six

313. To win the vacant WBO version of the world Heavyweight title Michael Moorer stopped Bert Cooper in which round?
    A. Four B. Five C. Six

314. **True or false,** Michael Moorer became the first boxer with the southpaw stance to hold a version of the world Heavyweight title?

315. On 16 May 1992 James Warring defended the IBF version of the world Cruiserweight title against Johnny Nelson and defeated him by which method?
    A. Four round stoppage B. Eight round knockout
    C. Twelve round points decision

316. Where did the above contest take place?
    A. America B. England C. Japan

317. In a previous bid for the world Cruiserweight crown Johnny Nelson challenged Carlos De Leon for which version of the championship?
    A. WBA B. IBF C. WBC

318. What was the result of the above contest?
    A. Twelve round draw B. points win for Nelson
    C. Points win for De Leon.

319. Where did the above contest take place?
    A. America B. England C. France

320. Who is the "Dark Destroyer"?
    A. Chris Eubank B. James Toney C. Nigel Benn.

321. To win the British Bantamweight title Drew Docherty stopped defending champion Joe Kelly in which round?
    A. Four B. Five C. Six

322 Where did the above contest take place?
    A. England B. Scotland C. Ireland

323. To win the IBF Flyweight crown Rodolfo Blanco defeated holder Dave McAuley by which method?
    A. Two round stoppage B. Five round knockout
    C. Twelve round points decision

324. Where did the above contest take place?
    A. Ireland B. England C. Spain

325. In defence of his world Heavyweight crown Evander Holyfield defeated Larry Holmes by which method?
    A. Five round stoppage B. Eight round knockout
    C. Twelve round points decision

326. Who was the referee of the above contest?
    A. Richard Steele B. Mills Lane C. Octavio Meyran

327. In which American city did the contest take place?
    A. Las Vegas B. San Francisco C. Reno

328. **True of false** during the contest Holyfield was down for a count in round one?

329. When was Prince Naseem Hamed's professional debut?
    A. 1992 B. 1993 C. 1994

330. To win the IBF Cruiserweight crown Alfred "Ice" Cole defeated James Warring by which method?
    A. One round stoppage B. Two round knockout
    C. Twelve round points decision

331. In defence of his IBF world Middleweight crown James Toney defeated Mike McCullum by which method on 29 August 1992?
    A. Four round stoppage B. Eight round knockout
    C. Twelve round points decision

332. In defence of his WBC Featherweight title Paul Hodkinson stopped challenger Fabrice Benichou in which round?
    A. Ten B. Eleven C. Twelve

333. In which country did the above contest take place?
    A. England B. Italy C. France

334. Fabrice Benichou was a former world IBF title holder in which weight division?
    A. Bantamweight B. Super-Bantamweight
    C. Featherweight

335. What was the result when Orlando Canizales defended his IBF Bantamweight title against challenger Samuel Duran?
    A. Points win for Duran B. Points win for Canizales
    C. Twelve round draw

336. In defence of his WBO world Flyweight title Pat Clinton defeated Danny Porter by which method?
    A. Two round stoppage B. Ten round knockout
    C. Twelve round points decision

337. Where did the above contest take place?
    A. London B. Glasgow C. Belfast

338. To win the IBF Intercontinental Flyweight crown on 18 February 1990 Joe Kelly stopped Reggie Brown in round eight. Where did this contest take place?
    A. Scotland B. America C. England

339. In which round did Ruben Palacio stop Colin McMillan to win the WBO Featherweight title?
    A. Five B. Six C. Eight

340. In which country did the above contest take place?
    A. England B. America C. Mexico

341. In which year was Roy Jones born?
    A. 1969 B. 1970 C. 1971

342. Who was Prince Naseem Hamed's first professional opponent?
    A. Ricky Beard B. Shaun Norman C. Andrew Bloomer

343. Hamed won the bout by a knockout in which round?
    A. One B. Two C. Three

344. In which year did Paul Weir make his professional debut?
   A. 1991 *B.* 1992 *C.* 1993

345. Who was his first professional opponent?
   A. Louis Veitch B. Eduardo Vallejo C. Neil Parry

346. Weir won by a knockout but in which round?
   A. One B. Two C. Three

347. Where did Weir's first contest take place?
   A. London B. Cardiff C. Glasgow

348. How many contests did Frank Bruno have in 1991?
   A. One B. Two C. Three

349. How many Lonsdale belts did Henry Cooper win outright for defences of his British Heavyweight title?
   A. One B. Two C. Three

350. To win the vacant WBO Lightweight title Giovanni Parisi stopped Javier Altamirano in which round?
   A. Eight B. Nine C. Ten

351. During 1992 Robbie Regan stopped opponent Juan Bautista in which round?
   A. One B. Two C. Three

352. To win the WBC version of the Super-Middleweight crown Nigel Benn forced defending champion Mauro Galvano to retire in which round?
   A. One B. Two C. Three

353. In which country did the above contest take place?
   A. England B. Italy C. Spain

354. *True or false* Benn was sent to the canvas for two counts of eight in the first round?

355. In a defence of his WBC Strawweight title Ricardo Lopez knocked out challenger Rocky Lim in which round?
   A. One B. Two C. Three

356. To win the WBO Super-Bantamweight crown Duke McKenzie defeated defending champion Jesse Benavides by which method?
A. Five round stoppage B. Eight round knockout
C. Twelve round points decision

357. Where did the above contest take place?
A. Mexico B. England C. America

358. In which round did Lloyd Honeyghan stop Carlo Colarusso during 1992?
A. Four B. Five C. Six

359. Where did the above contest take place?
A. Cardiff B. London C. Belfast

360. How many contests did Lloyd Honeyghan have in 1992?
A. One B. Two C. Three

361. To win the WBA version of the world Welterweight crown Crisanto Espana stopped Meldrick Taylor in which round?
A. Eight B. Nine C. Ten

362. In a Commonwealth title defence and a final Heavyweight eliminator Lennox Lewis stopped Donovan "Razor" Ruddock in which round?
A. One B. Two C. Three

363. In which country did the above contest take place?
A. Canada B. Australia C. England

364. To win the European Flyweight crown Robbie Regan defeated Salvatore Fanni by which method?
A. One round stoppage B. Two round knockout
C. Twelve round points decision

365. Where did the above contest take place?
A. Italy B. South Wales C. Spain

366. To win the world Heavyweight title Riddick Bowe defeated Evander Holyfield by which method?
A. Five round stoppage B. Eight round knockout
C. Twelve round points decision

367. Where did the above contest take place?
A. Las Vegas B. Reno C. Boston

368. Who was the referee of the above contest?
A. Mills Lane B. Richard Steele C. Joe Cortez

369. *True or false?* Lennox Lewis was awarded the WBC version of the world Heavyweight title in December 1992.

370. In defence of his WBC Super-Middleweight crown Nigel Benn stopped Nicky Piper in which round?
A. Nine B. Ten C. Eleven

371. To win the vacant British Flyweight title on 22 December 1992, how did Francis Ampofo defeat James Drummond?
A. One round stoppage B. Two round knockout
C. Twelve round points

372. To win the vacant WBA Penta-Continental Featherweight crown how did Steve Robinson defeat Paul Harvey?
A. Nine round stoppage B. Eleven round knockout
C. Twelve round points decision

373. Where did the above contest take place?
A. Cardiff B. Liverpool C. London

374. To win the Commonwealth Light-Middleweight title Lloyd Honeyghan stopped holder Mickey Hughes in which round in 1993?
A. Three B. Four C. Five

375. Who was the first man to regain the world Heavyweight title?
A. Muhammad Ali B. Floyd Patterson
C. Tim Witherspoon

376. In which year was Lloyd Honeyghan born?
A. *1960* B. *1961* C. *1962*

377. In defending his WBC world Featherweight title Paul Hodkinson forced challenger Ricardo Cepeda to retire in which round?
A. *Four* B. *Five* C. *Six*

378. In which country did the above contest take place?
A. *America* B. *England* C. *France*

379. What was the result when Gary Jacobs met Ludovic Proto for the vacant European Welterweight title on 16 October 1992?
A. *Points win for Jacobs* B. *Points win for Proto*
C. *A Twelve round draw*

380. In which country did the above contest take place?
A. *Scotland* B. *France* C. *England*

381. In which year did Andy Till make his professional debut?
A. *1986* B. *1987* C. *1988*

382. Who was the first man to win the world Heavyweight title three times?
A. *Floyd Patterson* B. *Muhammad Ali*
C. *Evander Holyfield*

383. In a return contest for the European Welterweight crown on 6 February 1993 Gary Jacobs and Ludovic Proto crossed gloves with the result being that one of them retired in round nine. *Which one was it?*

384. Where did the above contest take place?
A. *Italy* B. *Spain* C. *France*

385. In defence of his WBA & IBF world Heavyweight titles Riddick Bowe stopped Mike Dokes in which round?
A. *One* B. *Two* C. *Three*

386. Who was the referee of the above contest?
A. Mills Lane B. Joe Santarpia C. Richard Steele

387. Where did the above contest take place?
A. Las Vegas B. Boston C. New York

388. Mike Dokes was a former world Heavyweight champion, but which version of the title did he once hold?
A. IBF B. WBA C. WBC

389. In 1993 Adrian Stone outpointed Sean Daughtry over how many rounds?
A. Four B. Six C. Eight

390. In which round did Roy Jones stop opponent Glen Wolfe on 13 February 1993?
A. One B. Two C. Three

391. *True or false,* former European heavyweight champion Karl Mildenberger boxed in the southpaw stance?

392. In which round did Robert McCracken knockout Ernie Loveridge on 17 February 1993?
A. Three B. Four C. Five

393. To win the vacant WBO Cruiserweight title Tyrone Booze knocked out Derek Angol in which round?
A. Seven B. Eight C. Nine

394. In which country did the contest take place?
A. Germany B. England C. France

395. To win the vacant Commonwealth Heavyweight crown, how did Henry Akinwande defeat Jimmy Thunder?
A. Knockout in round two B. Knockout in round five
C. Twelve round points decision

396. In which country did the above contest take place?
A. England B. Australia C. New Zealand.

ROUND FIVE

397. In which round did Ray Close stop Vincenzo Nardiello to win the European Super-Middleweight crown?
A. Nine B. Ten C. Eleven

398. Which boxer is nick-named the "Dancing Destroyer"?
A. Lennox Lewis B. Henry Akinwande C. Herbie Hide

399. Noah Brusso was the real name of which former world Heavyweight champion?
A. Marvin Hart B. Tommy Burns C. James J. Braddock

400. On how many occasions did Chris Eubank defend his WBO Super-Middleweight title during 1992?
A. Three B. Four C. Five

401. During his professional career how many contests did Ezzard Charles have?
A. 120 B. 121 C. 122

402. In which year was Miguel Angel Gonzalez born?
A. 1969 B. 1970 C. 1971

403. When did Fidel Castro Smith make his professional debut?
A. 1985 B. 1986 C. 1987

404. During his career how many times did Bob Foster defend his world Light-Heavyweight title?
A. Twelve B. Thirteen C. Fourteen

405. When did Andy Holligan make his professional debut?
A. 1987 B. 1988 C. 1989

406. Who was his first professional opponent?
A. Jimmy Thornton B. Tony Richards C. Glyn Rhodes

407. Holligan won by outpointing his opponent over how many rounds?
A. Four B. Six C. Eight

408. In their contest during 1993 Lloyd Honeyghan and Vinny Pazienza fought in Atlantic City. What was the result?
A. Honeyghan retired in round ten
B. Pazienza was stopped in round ten
C. Honeyghan was knocked out in round ten

409. What was the nationality of former world Heavyweight contender Oscar Bonavena?
A. Mexican B. Argentinean C. German

410. To win the WBC Flyweight title during 1992 Yuri Arbachakov knocked defending champion Muangchai Kitikasem in which round?
A. Six B. Seven C. Eight

411. In which country did the above contest take place?
A. Japan B. France C. America

412. At this stage of his career Yuri Arbachakov was undefeated in how many professional contests?
A. Twelve B. Thirteen C. Fourteen

413. Who was nick-named the "Ambling Alp"?
A. Jack Sharkey B. Max Schmeling C. Primo Carnera

414. In his attempt to win the vacant WBC world Middleweight title Herol Graham was knocked out in which round by Julian Jackson?
A. Two B. Three C. Four

415. Where did the above contest take place?
A. Italy B. Spain C. England

416. In a previous attempt to win a version of the world crown Herol Graham was outpointed over twelve rounds by Mike McCallum. Was this also for a vacant crown, *Yes or No?*

417. Which version of the championship was Graham and McCallum contesting?
A. IBF B. WBC C. WBA

418. In which country did the above contest take place?
A. America B. England C. Italy

419. In which weight division was Troy Dorsey a world champion?
A. Bantamweight B. Super-Bantamweight
C. Featherweight.

420. To win the IBF world Light-Heavyweight title Henry Maske defeated Prince Charles Williams by which method?
A. Four round stoppage B. Eight round knockout
C. Twelve round points decision

421. During 1993 Tony Thornton outpointed John Scully over how many rounds?
A. Eight B. Ten C. Twelve

422. To win the vacant Welsh Super-Middleweight crown on 24 March 1993 Darron Griffiths stopped John Kaighin in which round?
A. Four B. Five C. Six

423. *True or false* Griffiths became the first holder of this title?

424. In 1993 Bert Cooper outpointed Derek Williams over how many rounds?
A. Eight B. Ten C. Twelve

425. In which country did the above contest take place?
A. England B. America C. Germany

426. *True or false* Derek Williams was a former European and Commonwealth Heavyweight champion?

427. In defence of his IBF Bantamweight crown on 27 March 1993 Orlando Canizales defeated Clarence Adams when he retired in which round?
A. Ten B. Eleven C. Twelve

428. In defence of his European Flyweight crown on 30 March 1993 Robbie Regan stopped Danny Porter in which round?
A. One B. Two C. Three

429. In his first professional contest Wayne McCullough stopped opponent Alfonso Zamora in which round?
A. Two B. Four C. Six

430. In the 1992 Olympic Games Wayne McCullough won a medal in the Bantamweight division, but what colour?
A. Gold B. Silver C. Bronze

431. In which round did Carl Thompson knock out Steve Harvey on 31 March 1993?
A. One B. Two C. Three

432. Over how many rounds did Kirkland Laing outpoint Newton Barnett on 31 March 1993?
A. Six B. Eight C. Ten

433. In defence of his WBO Light-Welterweight crown Carlos Gonzalez stopped Tony Baltazar in which round?
A. One B. Two C. Three

434. In which round did Tommy Morrison knockout Dan Murphy on 31 March 1993?
A. One B. Two C. Three

435. In defence of his WBA Light-Heavyweight crown Virgil Hill outpointed challenger Fabrice Tiozzo over twelve rounds on 3 April 1993. In which country did this contest take place?
A. America B. France C. Italy

436. In which round did Adrian Dodson stop opponent Chris Mulcahy on 31 March 1993?
A. One B. Two C. Three

437. To win the vacant Commonwealth Light-Heavyweight crown Brent Kosolofski stopped Michael Gale in which round?
A. Six B. Nine C. Twelve

438. In which round did Henry Wharton stop Ray Domenge in 1993?
A. One B. Two C. Three

439. In defence of his WBA Penta Continental Super-Middleweight crown Nicky Piper stopped challenger Chris Sande on 10 April 1993, in which round ?
A. Nine B. Ten C. Eleven

440. Where did the above contest take place?
A. Cardiff B. Swansea C. Port Talbot

441. In which year did Robin Reid make his professional debut?
A. 1993 B. 1994 C. 1995

442. At the 1992 Olympic Games Robin Reid won a medal in the Light-Middleweight division, but what colour was it?
A. Gold B. Silver C. Bronze

443. Who was Robin Reid's first opponent as a professional?
A. Mark Dawson B. Julian Eavis C. Andrew Furlong

444. Reid won his first bout by a stoppage but in which round?
A. One B. Two C. Three

445. Over how many rounds did Oscar De La Hoya outpoint Mike Grable in 1993?
A. Six B. Eight C. Ten

446. In defence of his WBO Bantamweight crown Rafael Del Valle stopped Wilfredo Vargas on 24 March 1993, in which round?
A. Four B. Five C. Six

447. In defence of his WBA Light-Welterweight title Juan Martin Coggi stopped Jose Rivera on 10 April 1993, in which round?
A. Seven B. Eight C. Nine

448. By which method did Vincenzo Belcastro retain his European Bantamweight crown against John Miceli on 7 April 1993?
A. Five round stoppage B. Nine round knockout
C. Twelve round points decision

449. To win the vacant WBO Featherweight title Steve Robinson defeated John Davison by which method?
A. Five round stoppage B. Nine round knockout
C. Twelve round points decision

450. *True or false* Robinson was down for two counts in the third round?

451. In defence of his British Light-Middleweight title Andy Till stopped Wally Swift Jnr on 14 April 1993, in which round?
A. Two B. Three C. Four

452. To win the vacant Southern Area Flyweight title Mickey Cantwell defeated opponent Darren Fifield by which method?
A. One round stoppage B. Five round knockout
C. Ten round points decision

453. During 1993 Michael Ayers challenged Giovanni Parisi for the WBO Lightweight crown. What was the result?
A. Points victory for Ayers B. Points victory for Parisi
C. Twelve round draw

454. In which country did the above contest take place?
   A. Italy B. England C. Germany

455. In which round did Sumbu Kalambay knockout Eddie Evans in 1993?
   A. One B. Two C. Three

456. *True or false* Sumbu Kalambay defeated Herol Graham twice in contests for the European Middleweight crown?

457. In 1993 Larry Holmes stopped Ken Lakusta in which round?
   A. Five B. Six C. Seven

458. In which round did James Toney stop Ricky Thomas on 17 April 1993?
   A. Eight B. Nine C. Ten

459. In defence of his IBF Super-Bantamweight crown during 1993 how did Kennedy McKinney defeat Richard Duran?
   A. Four round stoppage B. Nine round knockout
   C. Twelve round points decision

460. Julio Cesar Chavez knocked out opponent Silvio Rojas on 10 April 1993 in which round?
   A. One B. Two C. Three

461. In which round did Frank Bruno stop Carl "The Truth" Williams?
   A. Eight B. Nine C. Ten

462. In which country did the above contest take place?
   A. America B. France C. England

463. In defence of his WBA Super-Middleweight crown Michael Nunn stopped Crawford Ashley in which round?
   A. Four B. Five C. Six

464. In which country did the above contest take place?
   A. England B. America C. Spain

465. **True or false,** Lennox Lewis boxes in the southpaw stance?

466. Oliver McCall stopped Francesco Damiani in which round during their 1993 encounter?
A. Seven B. Eight C. Nine

467. How did Julio Cesar Vasquez retain his WBA Light-Middleweight crown against challenger Javier Castillejos?
A. Eight round stoppage B. Ten round knockout
C. Twelve round points decision

468. Gregorio Vargas won the WBC Featherweight title when defending champion Paul Hodkinson retired in which round?
A. Five B. Six C. Seven

469. Where did the above contest take place?
A. Dublin B. London C. Glasgow

470. In defence of his European Lightweight title Jean-Baptiste Mendy stopped Carl Crook in which round?
A. Eight B. Nine C. Ten

471. In his contest prior to the European challenge Crook had lost both his British and Commonwealth titles to Billy Schwer when he retired in which round?
A. Eight B. Nine C. Ten

472. Who is nick-named "The Grim Reaper"?
A. Frank Grant B. Robin Reid C. Richie Woodhall

473. To win the WBF Cruiserweight title Johnny Nelson stopped Dave Russell in which round?
A. Nine B. Ten C. Eleven

474. In which country did the above contest take place?
A. England C. France C. Australia

475. On 19 December 1992, Henry Akinwande boxed Axel Schulz for the vacant European Heavyweight title. What was the result?
   A. Twelve round draw B. Points win for Akinwande
   C. Points win for Schulz

476. In which country did the above contest take place?
   A. England B. Germany C. Italy

477. In defence of his WBC Lightweight crown Miguel "Angel" Gonzalez defeated Hector Lopez by which method?
   A. One round stoppage B. Eight round knockout
   C. Twelve round points decision

478. Over how many rounds did Tony Tubbs outpoint Melton Bowen in 1993?
   A. Six B. Eight C. Ten

479. In defence of his WBA Welterweight crown Cristanto Espana defeated Rodolfo Aguilar by which method?
   A. Nine round stoppage B. Ten round knockout
   C. Twelve round points decision

480. In which round did Adrian Dodson stop opponent Greg Wallace in 1993?
   A. One B. Two C. Three

481. In defence of his WBC Light-Welterweight crown Julio Cesar Chavez stopped Terrence Alli in which round?
   A. Four B. Five C. Six

482. In defence of his WBC Heavyweight crown Lennox Lewis defeated Tony Tucker by which method?
   A. Three round stoppage B. Eight round knockout
   C. Twelve round points decision

483. Tony Tucker was a former world Heavyweight champion. However which version of the title did he once hold?
   A. WBC B. WBA C. IBF

484. Gerald McClellan stopped champion Julian Jackson in which round on 8 May 1993 to win the WBC Middleweight crown?
A. Three B. Four C. Five

485. In defence of his WBA Middleweight title Reggie Johnson defeated Wayne Harris on 4 May 1993 by which method?
A. Two round stoppage B. Eight round knockout C. Twelve round points decision

486. In which round did Oscar De La Hoya force opponent Angelo Nunez to retire on 27 August 1993?
A. Five B. Six C. Seven

487. What was the result when Chris Eubank defended his WBO Super-Middleweight title against challenger Ray Close on 15 May 1993?
A. Points win for Eubank B. Points win for close C. Twelve round draw

488. Where did the above contest take place?
A. Belfast B. London C. Glasgow

489. To win the WBO Flyweight title Baby Jake Matlala stopped defending champion Pat Clinton in which round?
A. Six B. Seven C. Eight

490. Where did the above contest take place?
A. Glasgow B. Cardiff C. Belfast

491. To win the vacant WBO Strawweight title Paul Weir stopped opponent Fernando Martinez in which round?
A. Seven B. Eight C. Nine

492. Paul Weir was at this stage undefeated in how many contests?
A. Four B. Five C. Six

493. Paul Weir was the first European boxer to win a version of the world Strawweight title. *True or false?*

494. To win the vacant British Heavyweight title Herbie Hide stopped opponent Michael Murray on 27 February 1993, in which round?
A. Four B. Five C. Six

495. To win the vacant European Light-Heavyweight title Eddie Smulders stopped Yawe Davis on 12 May 1993, in which round?
A. Nine B. Ten C. Eleven

496. To win the vacant IBF Light-Welterweight title, how did Charles Murray defeat Rodney Moore?
A. Three round stoppage B. Nine round knockout
C. Twelve round points decision

497. To win the vacant WBO version of the world Middleweight title, how did Chris Pyatt defeat Sumbu Kalambay?
A. Four round stoppage B. Eight round knockout
C. Twelve round points decision

498. In which country did the above contest take place?
A. England B. Italy C. France

499. In defence of his Commonwealth Featherweight title Billy Hardy defeated opponent Barrington Francis by which method?
A. One round stoppage B. Two round knockout
C. Twelve round points decision

500. ***True or false,*** during the above contest Hardy was down for two counts in round Three.

501. In which country did the Hardy-Francis contest take place?
A. Canada B. England C. Australia

502. To win the vacant IBF Middleweight crown Roy Jones defeated opponent Bernard Hopkins by which method?
A. Two round stoppage B. Six round knockout C. Twelve round points decision

503. In defence of his WBA Heavyweight crown Riddick Bowe stopped challenger Jesse Ferguson in which round?
A. One B. Two C. Three

504. In which round did Andy Holligan stop opponent Lorenzo Garcia on 26 May 1993?
A. One B. Two C. Three

505. To win the vacant WBO world heavyweight title Tommy Morrison defeated George Foreman by which method?
A. Five Round Stoppage B. Eight Round Knockout C. Twelve Round Points Decision

506. During 1993 Oscar De La Hoya stopped Troy Dorsey in which round?
A. One B. Two C. Three

507. To win the WBO Light-Welterweight crown Zack Padilla defeated champion Carlos Gonzalez by which method?
A. Three Round Stoppage B. Eight Round Knockout C. Twelve Round Points Decision

508. Where did the above contest take place?
A. Atlantic City B. Los Angeles C. Las Vegas

509. In which year was Zack Padilla born?
A. 1963 B. 1964 C. 1965

510. Which title did Horace Notice not hold in the Heavyweight division?
A. British B. Commonwealth C. European

511. Over how many rounds did James Toney outpoint Glenn Thomas during 1993?
A. Eight B. Ten C. Twelve

512. Daniel Jimenez defeated Duke McKenzie by which method to win the WBO Super-Bantamweight title?
A. One Round Knockout B. Four Round Stoppage C. Twelve Round Points Decision

513. Over how many rounds did Johnny Armour outpoint Boualem Belkif on 9 June 1993?
A. Six B. Eight C. Ten

514. At this stage Johnny Armour was undefeated in how many professional contests?
A. Ten B. Twelve C. Thirteen

515. In defence of his WBO Bantamweight crown Rafael Del Valle defeated challenger Miguel Lora by which method?
A. Three Round stoppage B. Nine Round Knockout C. Twelve Round points decision

516. In which year was Rafael Del Valle born?
A. 1967 B. 1968 C. 1969

517. In defence of his WBA Flyweight crown David Griman stopped challenger Hiroki Ioka in which round?
A. Six B. Seven C. Eight

518. In which country did the above contest take place?
A. Mexico B. America C. Japan

519. During 1993 Terry Norris defended his WBC Light-Middleweight title against Troy Waters and forced him to retire in which round?
A. One B. Two C. Three

520. Where did the above contest take place?
A. San Diego B. Las Vegas C. Mexico City

521. **True or false,** Terry Norris was down for a count in round two?

522. To win the IBF Welterweight crown Felix Trinidad knocked out defending champion Maurice Blocker in which round?
A. One B. Two C. Three

523. At this stage of his career Felix Trinidad was undefeated in how many professional contests?
A. Twenty B. Twenty one C. Twenty two

524. In defence of his WBC Super-middleweight crown Nigel Benn stopped challenger Lou Gent in which round?
A. Two B. Three C. Four

525. **True or false,** Benn was down for a count in round two?

526. Where did the Benn - Gent contest take place?
A. Earls Court B. Muswell Hill C. Brentwood

527. To win the vacant WBO Penta-Continental Middleweight title Steve Collins stopped Gerhard Botes in which round?
A. Five B. Six C. Seven

528. Where did the above contest take place?
A. England B. America C. Italy

529. During 1993 Robbie Regan outpointed Adrian Ochoa over how many rounds?
A. Six B. Eight C. Ten

530. Where did the above contest take place?
A. Cardiff B. Earls Court C. Glasgow

531. To win the vacant European Cruiserweight title, Massimiliano Duran knocked out Derek Angol in which round?
A. Nine B. Ten C. Eleven

532. In which country did the above contest take place?
A. Italy B. France C. England

533. To win the vacant Commonwealth Flyweight crown Francis Ampofo knocked out Albert Musankabala in which round?
A. One B. Two C. Three

534. Where did the above contest take place?
A. England B. South Africa. C. Australia

535. In which round did Robert McCracken stop Steve Langley in 1993?
A. Three B. Four C. Five

536. In defence of his WBC Strawweight title Ricardo Lopez stopped challenger Saman Sorjaturong in which round?
A. One B. Two C. Three

537. Where did the above contest take place?
A. Nuevo Laredo B. Lake Tahoe C. Las Vegas

538. In defence of his WBO Featherweight crown Steve Robinson knocked out Sean Murphy in which Round?
A. Seven B. Eight C. Nine

539. *True or false,* Robinson was down for a count in round three?

540. Where did the Robinson - Murphy contest take place?
A. Cardiff B. Swansea C. Llanelli

541. In defence of his IBF Cruiserweight crown Alfred "Ice" Cole defeated Glenn McCrory by which method?
A. Two round stoppage B. Nine round knockout
C. Twelve round points decision

542. *True or false,* Cole was down twice for a count in round one?

543. Where did the Cole - McCrory contest take place?
A. Russia B. England C. America

544. In defence of his IBF Super-Bantamweight Crown Kennedy McKinney stopped challenger Rudy Zavala in which round?
A. One B. Two C. Three

545. Where did the above contest take place?
A. Memphis B. Las Vegas C. Atlantic City

546. In defence of his WBC Flyweight title Yuri Arbachakov defeated challenger Ysaias Zamudio by which method?
A. Four round stoppage B. Eight round knockout
C. Twelve round points decision

547. What was the nick-name of Henry Cooper's famed left hook?
A. Cooper's Sleeper B. Enery's 'Ammer C. Henry's Bomb

548. At which weight was J.B.Williamson a WBC world champion?
A. Middle B. Light-Heavy C. Heavy

549. How many successful defences of the world Heavyweight title did Rocky Marciano make?
A. Four B. Five C. Six

550. In defence of his IBF and WBC Light-Flyweight titles Michael Carbajal knocked out Kwang-Sun Kim in which round?
A. Seven B. Eight C. Nine

551. Where did the above contest take place?
A. Atlantic City B. Reno C. Las Vegas

552. To win the WBC version of the world Bantamweight crown Il-Jung Byun defeated defending champion Victor Rabanales by which method?
A. A five round stoppage B. Eight round knockout.
C. Twelve round points decision

553. In defence of his IBF Lightweight crown Freddie Pendleton defeated Jorge Paez by which method?
A. Eight round knockout B. Eleven round stoppage C. Twelve round points decision

554. In which year was Thomas Hearns born?
A. 1958 B. 1959 C. 1960

555. Which former world Heavyweight champion was nick-named the Brown Bomber ?
A. Jack Johnson B. Joe Louis C. Ezzard Charles

556. In defence of the British Super-Featherweight title Neil Haddock stopped Steve Walker in which round?
A. Five B. Six C. Seven

557. Where did the above contest take place?
A. Oldham B. Liverpool C. Llanelli

558. Neil Haddock won the British Super-Featherweight title when he stopped defending champion Michael Armstrong in which round?
A. Four B. Five C. Six

559. In which year did the above contest take place?
A. 1991 B. 1992 C. 1993

560. In which round did John Ashton retire when he tried to win the British Middleweight crown held by Frank Grant?
A. Five B. Six C. Seven

561. Where did the above contest take place?
A. Leeds B. Bradford C. Manchester

562. To win the British Middleweight crown Frank Grant defeated Herol Graham when he stopped him in which round?
A. Seven B. Eight C. Nine

563. **True or false,** Grant became the first British boxer in the professional ranks to defeat Graham?

564. In which round did Carl Thompson knock out Willie Jake during 1993 ?
    A. One B. Two C. Three

565. Over how many rounds did Paul Burke outpoint opponent Lyndon Paul Walker in 1993?
    A. Six B. Eight C. Ten

566. Over how many rounds did Maurice Core outpoint opponent John Kaighin during 1993?
    A. Six B. Eight C. Ten

567. In defence of his IBF Light-Welterweight crown Charles Murray defeated Juan Laporte by which method?
    A. Stopped in round four B. Disqualification in round ten
    C. Twelve round points decision

568. In defence of his WBA Light-Flyweight title Myung Woo Yuh defeated challenger Yuichi Hosono by which method?
    A. Six round stoppage B. Nine round knockout
    C. Twelve round points decision

569. Pernell Whitaker retained his WBC Welterweight title against Julio Cesar Chavez by which method during 1993?
    A. Eight round stoppage B. Twelve round points decision
    C. Twelve round draw

570. Where did the above contest take place?
    A. New York B. San Antonio C. Atlantic City

571. How did Azumah Nelson retain his WBC Super-Featherweight title against Jesse James Leija on 10 September 1993?
    A. Two round stoppage B. Nine round knockout
    C. Twelve round draw

572. In defence of his WBC Light-Middleweight crown Terry Norris knocked out challenger Joe Gatti in which round?
A. One B. Two C. Three

573. In which round did Danny Garcia retire in the non-title contest against James Toney during 1993?
A. Five B. Six C. Seven

574. In which weight division was David Kotey a WBC world title holder?
A. Bantamweight B. Featherweight C. Lightweight

575. In which round did Kirkland Laing stop Dean Cooper in 1993?
A. Five B. Six C. Seven

576. In defence of his WBC Middleweight title Gerald McClellan knocked out challenger Jay Bell in which round?
A. One B. Four C. Six

577. In defence of his IBF Welterweight crown Felix Trinidad knocked out Luis Garcia in which round?
A. One B. Two C. Three

578. Over how many rounds did Mike McCallum outpoint Glenn Thomas in 1993?
A. Six B. Eight C. Ten

579. In which round did Fidel Castro Smith stop Karl Barwise in 1993?
A. Six B. Seven C. Eight

580. In which round did Gary Logan knock out Paul King in their contest which took place on 28 November 1993?
A. Two B. Three C. Four

581. In defence of his WBF Cruiserweight crown Johnny Nelson stopped challenger Tom Collins in which round?
A. One B. Five C. Eight

582. Where did the above contest take place?
   A. Mansfield B. Brentwood C. Halifax

583. *True or false,* Tom Collins was a former European and British Light-Heavyweight champion?

584. To win the vacant European Heavyweight title Henry Akinwande defeated Axel Schulz by which method?
   A. Five round stoppage B. Nine round knockout
   C. Twelve round points decision

585. Where did the above contest take place?
   A. England B. Germany C. Spain

586. In which month during 1993 did this contest take place?
   A. March B. May C. July

587. Who was the last holder of the European Heavyweight crown prior to Henry Akinwande?
   A. Herbie Hide B. Lennox Lewis C. Jean-Maurice Chanet

588. In which round did Roy Jones knockout opponent Sugar Boy Malinga in 1993?
   A. Four B. Five C. Six

589. In defence of his WBC Lightweight Crown Miguel "Angel" Gonzalez defeated David Sample by which method?
   A. Two round stoppage B. Eight round knockout
   C. Twelve round points decision

590. In which round did Oscar De La Hoya stop opponent Renaldo Carter in 1993?
   A. Five B. Six C. Seven

591. In which round did Ray Mercer knock out Tony Willis on 12 August 1993?
   A. One B. Two C. Three

592. Where did the above contest take place?
   A. New York B. Atlantic City C. Mississippi

593. Whose middle name is Claudius?
   A. Chris Eubank B. Robbie Regan C. Lennox Lewis

594. In defence of his WBA Light-Welterweight title against Jose Barbosa, Juan Martin Coggi retained his crown by which method?
   A. One round stoppage B. Five round retirement.
   C. Twelve round points decision

595. In defence of his WBA Light-Heavyweight title against challenger Sergio Merani, Virgil Hill retained his championship by which method?
   A. Five round stoppage B. Eight round retirement
   C. Twelve round points decision

596. In their 1993 encounter Roberto Duran stopped opponent Sean Fitzgerald in which round?
   A. Four B. Five C. Six

597. In which round did Iran Barkley stop Ed "Dino" Stewart in their 1993 meeting?
   A. Seven B. Eight C. Nine

598. In defence of his IBF Super-Flyweight crown Julio Cesar Borboa knocked out Carlos Mercado in which round?
   A. One B. Two C. Three

599. In defence of his WBA Light-Middleweight crown Julio Cesar Vasquez retained his title against challenger Aaron Davis by which method?
   A. Six round retirement B. Twelve round draw
   C. Twelve round points decision

600. Aaron Davis was a former WBA world champion in which weight division?
   A. Welterweight B. Light-Middleweight C. Middleweight

601. ***True or false,*** Lloyd Honeyghan once outpointed Aaron Davis over ten rounds?

602. Where was Felix Trinidad born?
     A. America B. Mexico C. Puerto Rico

603. Who was the first holder of the Commonwealth Light-Welterweight title?
     A. Hector Thompson B. Jeff Malcolm C. Joe Tetteh

604. Which Commonwealth crown did Joe Bygraves hold during his career? (then called Empire title).
     A. Middle B. Light-Heavy C. Heavy

605. In which year was Paul Burke born?
     A. 1966 B. 1967 C. 1968

606. Kyun-Yung Park retained his WBA Featherweight title against Tae-Shik Chun by which method in 1993?
     A. Five round stoppage B. Nine round knockout
     C. Twelve round points decision

607. Tom Johnson retained his IBF Featherweight crown by which method against challenger Sugar Baby Rojas?
     A. Five round retirement B. Twelve round draw
     C. Twelve Round points decision

608. How did Chana Porpaoin retain his WBA Strawweight title against Ronnie Magramo on 22 August 1993?
     A. One round stoppage B. Five round knockout
     C. Twelve round points decision

609. In which country did the above contest take place?
     A. Mexico B. Thailand C. America

610. In which round did Chris Pyatt knockout Hugo Corti in defence of his WBO world Middleweight crown?
     A. Five B. Six C. Seven

611. In which weight division was Bernard Benton a WBC world champion?
    A. Light-Heavyweight B. Cruiserweight C. Heavyweight

612. In the film Rocky V a future world Heavyweight champion appeared in a main role. Name him.
    A. Tommy Morrison B. Lennox Lewis C. Herbie Hide

613. Prior to his challenge for Joe Louis's world Heavyweight crown which challenger is reputed to have said "I will moider da bum"?
    A. Tami Mauriello B. Tony Galento C. Jersey Joe Walcott

614. In which year was Nigel Benn born?
    A. 1963 B. 1964 C. 1965

615. Which world title did Kuniaki Shibata **not** hold during his professional career?
    A. Bantamweight B. Featherweight
    C. Super-Featherweight

616. Who was the "Clones Cyclone"?
    A. Howard Winstone B. Paul Hodkinson
    C. Barry McGuigan

617. By which method did James Cook defeat Fidel Castro Smith to win the vacant British Super-Middleweight title?
    A. One round stoppage B. Five round knockout
    C. Twelve Round points decision

618. Where did the above contest take place?
    A. Southwark B. Battersea C. Catford

619. *True or false,* James Cook was a former European Super-middleweight champion?

620. *True or false,* Nigel Benn held the British Middleweight title before going on to win a version of the world crown?

621. In which round did Kirkland Laing stop opponent Dave Maj on 15 September 1993?
A. One B. Two C. Three

622. To win the vacant WBC international Light-Flyweight crown Pablo Tiznado defeated Mickey Cantwell by which method?
A. One round stoppage B. Three round knockout
C. Twelve round points decision

623. Where did the above contest take place?
A. Mexico B. England C. France

624. In defence of his IBF Light-Heavyweight title Henry Maske defeated challenger Anthony Hembrick by which method?
A. Three round knockout B. Eight round stoppage
C. Twelve Round points decision

625. Joe Louis is reputed to have said "he can run but he can't hide" before defending his world Heavyweight title against which challenger?
A. Billy Conn B. Tommy Farr C. Arturo Godoy

626. In defence of his WBO Super-Featherweight crown Jimmy Bredahl defeated challenger Renato Cornett by which method?
A. Two round knockout B. Ten round stoppage
C. Twelve Round points decision

627. In which country did the above contest take place?
A. Austria B. Denmark C. Germany

628. In which round did Wayne McCullough stop opponent Boualem Belkif during 1993?
A. Three B. Four C. Five

629. In which round did Prince Naseem Hamed knockout Chris Clarkson on 24 September 1993?
A. One B. Two C. Three

630. In defence of his European Welterweight title Gary Jacobs stopped challenger Daniel Bicchieray in which round?
A. Five B. Six C. Seven

631. In which country did the above contest take place?
A. France B. Scotland C. England

632. On 22 September 1993 J.A. Bugner knocked out opponent Gary Charlton in which round?
A. One B. Two C. Three

633. *True or false,* J.A. Bugner is the son of former European, British and Commonwealth Heavyweight champion, Joe Bugner?

634. To win the vacant British Welterweight crown Del Bryan defeated opponent Pat Barrett by which method?
A. Three round stoppage B. Eight round knockout
C. Twelve Round points decision

635. In which round did Adrian Dodson knockout opponent Robert Peel on 22 September 1993?
A. One B. Two C. Three

636. In defence of his WBC Super-Bantamweight Crown Tracy Harris Patterson stopped Daniel Zaragoza in which round?
A. Six B. Seven C. Eight

637. *Yes or no,* Tracy Harris Patterson is the adopted son of former world Heavyweight champion Floyd Patterson.

638. By which method did Giovanni Parisi retain his WBO Lightweight title against challenger Antonio Rivera?
A. Five round retirement B. Twelve round draw
C. Twelve Round points decision

639. In defence of his WBA Light-Welterweight Crown Juan Martin Coggi stopped Guillermo Cruz in which round?
A. Ten B. Eleven C. Twelve

640. What was the result when Luigi Camputaro and Salvatore Fanni contested the vacant European Flyweight title on 22 September 1993?
A. Points win for Camputaro B. Points win for Fanni
C. Twelve Round draw

641. In defence of his IBF Strawweight title Ratanapol Sowvoraphin stopped Domingus Siwalete in which round?
A. Two B. Three C. Four

642. In which country did the above contest take place?
A. Japan B. America C. Thailand

643. Which European crown did Tom Bogs not hold during his professional career?
A. Middleweight B. Light-Heavyweight C. Heavyweight

644. In defence of his WBC Heavyweight crown Lennox Lewis stopped Frank Bruno in which round?
A. Five B. Six C. Seven

645. Where did the above contest take place?
A. Cardiff B. Llanelli C. Swansea

646. *True or false,* this was the first world Heavyweight title to involve two British fighters?

647. Lennox Lewis was floored for a count in this contest. *Yes or no?*

648. Frank Bruno was floored for a count in round two. *Yes or no?*

649. At this stage of his career Lennox Lewis was now undefeated in how many contests?
A. Twenty Three B. Twenty Four C. Twenty Five

650. How many bouts did Frank Bruno have during 1993?
A. One B. Two C. Three

651. By which method did Leonzer Barber retain his WBO Light-Heavyweight crown against Andrea Magi?
A. One round stoppage *B. Two round knockout*
C. Twelve Round points decision

652. To win the WBA world Middleweight crown John David Jackson defeated defending champion Reggie Johnson by which method?
A. Five round stoppage *B. Eight round knockout.*
C. Twelve round points decision.

653. In which country did the above contest take place?
A. Argentina *B. America* *C. France*

654. John David Jackson once held which version of the world Light- Middleweight title?
A. WBC *B. WBO* *C. WBA*

655. What was the result when Nigel Benn met Chris Eubank for the WBC and WBO Super-Middleweight titles on 9 October 1993?
A. Points win for Eubank *B. Points win for Benn*
C. Twelve round draw

656. *True or false,* Benn was floored for a count in round Two?

657. *True or false,* Eubank was floored for a count in round Four?

658. Where did the above contest take place?
A. London *B. Manchester* *C. Glasgow*

659. How many contests did Nigel Benn have in 1993?
A. One *B. Two* *C. Three*

660. How many contests did Chris Eubank have in 1993?
A. One *B. Two* *C. Three*

661. In defence of his WBA Welterweight title Crisanto Espana stopped challenger Donovan Boucher in which round?
A. *Eight* B. *Nine* C. *Ten*

662. To win the vacant Commonwealth flyweight title Darren Fifield stopped Danny Porter in which round on the 13th October 1993?
A. *Nine* B. *Ten* C. *Eleven*

663. To win the WBO version of the world Heavyweight title Michael Bentt stopped defending champion Tommy Morrison in which round?
A. *One* B. *Two* C. *Three*

664. Where did the above contest take place?
A. *New York* B. *Atlantic City* C. *Tulsa*

665. In which country was Michael Bentt born?
A. *America* B. *Canada* C. *England*

666. In defence of his IBF Super-middleweight Crown James Toney defeated Tony Thornton by which method?
A. *Two round stoppage* B. *Five round knockout*
C. *Twelve round points decision*

667. On 26 October 1993 Vinny Pazienza outpointed Robbie Sims over how many rounds?
A. *Eight* B. *Ten* C. *Twelve*

668. *True or false*, Robbie Sims is the half-brother of former world middle-weight champion Marvin Hagler?

669. Johnny Bredahl retained his WBO Super-Flyweight crown against challenger Eduardo Nazario on the 29th October 1993 by a disqualification in which round?
A. *Two* B. *Three* C. *Four*

670. In which round did Oscar De La Hoya knock out opponent Narciso Valenzuela on 30 October 1993?
A. *One* B. *Two* C. *Three*

671. In defence of his WBO Super-Bantamweight crown Daniel Jimenez stopped Felix Garcia Losada in which round?
A. Three B. Four C. Five

672. In a non-title contest Julio Cesar Vasquez stopped opponent Han Kim in which round on 1 October 1993?
A. Three B. Four C. Five

673. In defence of his Penta Continental Heavyweight crown Herbie Hide stopped Mike Dixon in which round?
A. Eight B. Nine C. Ten

674. *True or false,* Herbie Hide was floored twice in the first round?

675. Where did the Hide-Dixon contest take place?
A. Bethnal Green B. Norwich C. Cardiff

676. At this stage of his career Herbie Hide was undefeated in how many contests?
A. 22 B. 23 C. 24

677. In defence of his WBC & IBF Light-Flyweight titles Michael Carbajal stopped challenger Domingo Sosa in which round?
A. Four B. Five C. Six

678. Over how many rounds did Mickey Cantwell outpoint Anthony Hanna on 3 November 1993?
A. Six B. Eight C. Ten

679. In which round did Lloyd Honeyghan stop opponent Steve Goodwin on 2 November 1993?
A. Four B. Five C. Six

680. Over how many rounds did James Cook outpoint opponent Tony Booth on 7 September 1992?
A. Six B. Eight C. Ten

681. Over how many rounds did James "Buddy" McGirt outpoint Nick Rupa on 2 November 1993?
A. Eight B. Ten C. Twelve

682. In which round did Valery Kayumba stop opponent Angel Cordova on 6 November 1993?
A. Six B. Seven C. Eight

683. To win the vacant WBA Cruiserweight title Orlin Norris knocked out opponent Marcelo Figueroa in which round?
A. Six B. Seven C. Eight

684. *True or false,* Norris is the brother of Terry Norris?

685. Evander Holyfield regained the IBF and WBA versions of the world Heavyweight title when he defeated Riddick Bowe by which method?
A. Three round stoppage B. Eight round knockout
C. Twelve round points decision

686. Who was the referee of the above contest?
A. Mills Lane B. Vic Drakulich C. Marty Coscino

687. Where did the above contest take place?
A. Reno B. San Francisco C. Las Vegas

688. This was the first time that Riddick Bowe had been defeated in the professional ranks. *True or false?*

689. In which round did Thomas Hearns knockout opponent Andrew Maynard on 6 November 1993?
A. One B. Two C. Three

690. In which round did Neville Brown stop Frank Grant when challenging for the British Middleweight championship on 10 November 1993?
A. Five B. Six C. Seven

691. Where did the above contest take place?
A. Bethnal Green B. Wolverhampton C. Dewsbury

692. At this stage of his career how many professional contests had Neville Brown taken part in?
    A. 20 B. 21 C. 22

693. Over how many rounds did Calvin Grove outpoint Pete Taliaferro in 1993?
    A. Eight B. Ten C. Twelve

694. In defence of his WBA Light-Heavyweight title Virgil Hill stopped challenger Saul Montana in which round?
    A. Eight B. Nine C. Ten

695. In which round did Wayne McCullough knockout opponent Andres Gonzalez on 16 November 1993?
    A. One **B.** Two **C.** Three

696. At this stage of his career Wayne McCullough was undefeated in how many contests?
    A. Seven B. Eight C. Nine

697. Jose Luis Bueno won the WBC version of the Super-Flyweight title when he defeated defending champion Sung-Il Moon by which method?
    A. One round stoppage B. Three round knockout
    C. Twelve Round points decision

698. On 19 November 1993 Ray Mercer defeated opponent Jesse Ferguson when he outpointed him over how many rounds?
    A. Eight B. Ten C. Twelve

699. Who was the referee of the above contest?
    A. Tony Orlando B. Mills Lane C. Bernie Soto

700. Where did the above contest take place?
    A. Las Vegas B. Atlantic City C. Reno

701. In defence of his IBF Light-Welterweight title Charles Murray met challenger Courtney Hooper and retained the championship by a retirement win in which round?
A. Five B. Six C. Seven

702. In which weight division was Chic Calderwood a British champion?
A. Middleweight B. Light-Heavyweight C. Heavyweight

703. Which British title did Bunny Johnson not hold during his professional career?
A. Middleweight B. Light-Heavyweight. C. Heavyweight

704. Which version of the world Featherweight title did Jose Legra hold during his career?
A. WBC B. WBA C. IBF

705. Johnny Nelson won the WBF Heavyweight crown when he defeated holder Jimmy Thunder by which method?
A. Four round stoppage B. Nine round knockout
C. Twelve Round points decision

706. Where did the above contest take place?
A. Australia B. England C. New Zealand

707. Zack Padilla retained his WBO world Light-Welterweight crown when Efrem Calamati retired in which round?
A. Seven B. Eight C. Nine

708. In defence of his IBF Cruiserweight title Alfred "Ice" Cole stopped challenger Vincent Boulware in which round?
A. Four B. Five C. Six

709. Where did the above contest take place?
A. Atlantic City B. Las Vegas C. New York

710. In defence of his WBC Cruiserweight crown Anaclet Wamba retained the championship when challenger Akim Tafer retired in which round?
A. Seven B. Eight C. Nine

711. Orlando Canizales retained his IBF Bantamweight crown when he defeated Juvenal Berrio by which method?
A. One round knockout B. Two round stoppage
C. Twelve round points

712. On 20 November 1993 Nestor Giovannini defended his WBO version of the world Cruiserweight title against Markus Bott and retained his crown by which method?
A. One round stoppage B. Twelve round draw
C. Twelve round points decision

713. In which country did the above contest take place?
A. Argentina B. Germany C. Denmark

714. Vincenzo Nardiello won the vacant European Super-Middleweight title when he defeated Mauro Galvano by which method?
A. Eight round stoppage B. Ten round knockout
C. Twelve round points decision

715. To retain his WBC world Lightweight Crown Miguel "Angel" Gonzalez stopped Wilfredo Rocha in which round?
A. Nine B. Ten C. Eleven

716. Where did the above contest take place?
A. Guadalajara B. Mexico City C. Aguascalientes

717. Wilfredo Vasquez retained his WBA Super-Bantamweight title when he defeated Hiroki Yokota by which method?
A. Three round retirement B. Twelve round draw
C. Twelve round points decision

718. Where did the above contest take place?
A. Japan B. France C. Italy

719. In which round did Henry Akinwande stop Biagio Chianese in defence of his European Heavyweight title?
A. Three B. Four C. Five

720. In which country did the above contest take place?
A. Italy B. France C. England

721. At this stage of his career Henry Akinwande was undefeated in how many professional contests?
A. Twenty one B. Twenty two C. Twenty three

722. Billy Schwer regained his British and Commonwealth Lightweight titles when he defeated Paul Burke by which method?
A. One round stoppage B. Eight round knockout
C. Twelve round points decision

723. On which date did the above contest take place?
A. 10 October 1993 B. 10 November 1993
C. 10 December 1993

724. Billy Schwer had lost these titles to Paul Burke in a previous contest when he was stopped in which round?
A. Five B. Six C. Seven

725. On which date did the above contest take place?
A. 24 February 1993 B. 24 March 1993
C. 24 April 1993

726. In defence of his British Light-Heavyweight crown Maurice Core stopped challenger Simon Harris in which round?
A. Nine B. Ten C. Eleven

727. In defence of his WBO Penta-Continental Middleweight title Steve Collins stopped Wayne Ellis in which round?
A. Nine B. Ten C. Eleven

728. Where did the above contest take place?
A. Swansea B. Llanelli C. Cardiff

729. To retain his WBA Strawweight crown Chana Porpaoin knocked out challenger Rafael Torres in which round?
A. Two B. Three C. Four

730. In defence of his IBF Featherweight title Tom "Boom Boom" Johnson stopped Stephane Haccoun in which round?
A. Eight B. Nine C. Ten

731. Where did the above contest take place?
A. France B. Italy C. America

732. Eloy Rojas won the WBA Featherweight crown when he defeated holder Kyun-Yung Park by which method?
A. Two round stoppage B. Four round knockout
C. Twelve round points decision

733. Kevin Kelley won the WBC Featherweight title when he defeated holder Gregorio "Goyo" Vargas by which method?
A. Three round stoppage B. Eight round knockout
C. Twelve round points decision

734. Where did the above contest take place?
A. Atlantic City B. Reno C. Las Vegas

735. At this stage of his career Kevin Kelley was undefeated in how many professional contests?
A. 35 B. 36 C. 37

736. Michael Moorer outpointed opponent Mike Evans over how many rounds on 4 December 1993?
A. Eight B. Ten C. Twelve

737. Roy Jones outpointed Fermin Chirino over how many rounds on 30 November 1993?
A. Eight B. Ten C. Twelve

738. In defence of his WBC international Heavyweight crown Herbie Hide knocked out Jeff Lampkin in which round?
A. One B. Two C. Three

739. **True or false,** Herbie Hide was down for two counts in round one?

740. Where did the Hide - Lampkin contest take place?
A. England B. South Africa C. America

741. Jeff Lampkin was a former world Cruiserweight champion. However, which version of the title did he once hold?
A. WBC B. IBF C. WBA

742. Which champion did Jeff Lampkin defeat to win the crown?
A. Glenn McCrory B. Robert Daniels
C. Masimilliano Duran

743. In which year did Lampkin win the Cruiserweight crown?
A. 1990 B. 1992 C. 1993

744. Baby Jake Matlala retained his WBO Flyweight title when challenger Luigi Camputaro retired in which round?
A. Seven. B. Eight. C. Nine.

745. In which country did the above contest take place?
A. Italy B. America C. South Africa

746. Tommy Burns is the shortest man to win the world Heavyweight crown. How tall was he?
A. 5 ft. 6 inches B. 5 ft. 7 inches C. 5 ft. 8 inches

747. In defence of his IBF Light-Heavyweight crown Henry Maske retained his championship against challenger David Vedder by which method?
A. Two round retirement B. Twelve round draw
C. Twelve round points decision

748. In which country did the above contest take place?
A. America B. Spain C. Germany

749. To retain his IBF Strawweight title Rantanapol Sowvoraphin stopped Felix Naranjo in which round?
A. Two B. Three C. Four

750. Nigel Benn is a cousin of soccer player Paul Ince. *True or false?*

751. In defence of his WBC Flyweight title against Ysaias Zamudio, Yuri Arbachakov retained the championship by which method?
A. Five round stoppage B. Six round knockout
C. Twelve round points decision

752. To win the vacant British Featherweight title Duke McKenzie stopped opponent John Davison in which round?
A. Two B. Three C. Four

753. Where was the above contest held?
A. Manchester B. London C. Glasgow

754. What was the result when Robin Reid crossed gloves with opponent Danny Juma on 18 December 1993?
A. Points victory for Reid B. Points victory for Juma
C. A draw

755. How many rounds did Reid and Juma box in the above contest?
A. Four B. Five C. Six

756. In which Round did Joe Calzaghe stop opponent Spencer Alton on 16 December 1993?
A. One B. Two C. Three

757. To win the vacant WBO Penta-Continental Light-Heavyweight crown Garry Delaney stopped opponent Ray Albert in which round?
A. One B. Two C. Three

758. At this stage of his career Garry Delaney was undefeated in how many contests?
A. Fifteen B. Sixteen C. Seventeen

759. To win the WBC Light-Middleweight title Simon Brown knocked out holder Terry Norris in which round?
A. Three B. Four C. Five

760. To retain his WBA Super-Middleweight crown Michael Nunn defeated challenger Merqui Sosa by which method?
A. Two round stoppage B. Eleven round knockout
C. Twelve round points decision

761. In which round did Oliver McCall stop opponent Art Card on 18 December 1993?
A. One **B.** Two **C.** Three

762. In which round did Tony Tucker stop opponent David Graves on 18 December 1993?
A. One B. Two C. Three

763. Julio Cesar Chavez retained his WBC Light-Welterweight crown against Andy Holligan who retired in which round?
A. Three B. Four C. Five

764. *True or false,* Holligan was down for a count in round one?

765. Where did the Chavez - Holligan contest take place?
A. Puebla B. Mexico City C. Las Vegas

766. Andy Holligan, a British and Commonwealth Light-Welterweight champion at the time of the challenge, won these titles when he defeated holder Tony Ekubia on 20 June 1991 by which method?
A. Four round stoppage B. Six round knockout
C. Twelve round points decision

767. In which round did Roberto Duran stop opponent Tony Menefee on 14 December 1993?
A. Seven B. Eight C. Nine

768. At this stage of his career Roberto Duran had taken part in how many professional contests?
A. 99 B. 100 C. 101

769. To retain his WBC Strawweight title Ricardo Lopez knocked out Manny Melchor in which round?
A. Ten   B. Eleven   C. Twelve

770. In defence of his WBO Light-Welterweight title Zack Padilla defeated Ray Oliveira by which method?
A. One round stoppage   B. Six round retirement
C. Twelve round points decision

771. In defence of his WBA Light-Heavyweight crown Virgil Hill defeated challenger Guy Waters by which method?
A. Two round stoppage   B. Six round knockout
C. Twelve round points decision

772. How many defences of the WBA Light-Heavyweight title did Virgil Hill make in 1993?
A. Four   B. Five   C. Six

773. What is the nickname given to Roberto Duran?
A. Mr. Knockout   B. The punisher   C. Hands of Stone

774. To win the vacant WBO Strawweight crown Alex Sanchez stopped opponent Orlando Malone in which round?
A. One   B. Two   C. Three

775. In the first defence of the WBO Strawweight title Alex Sanchez stopped Arturo Garcia Mayen in which round?
A. One   B. Two   C. Three

776. In defence of his WBA Light-Welterweight title Juan Martin Coggi stopped challenger Eder Gonzalez in which round on 17 December 1993?
A. Six   B. Seven   C. Eight

777. Junior Jones retained his WBA Bantamweight crown against challenger Elvis Alvarez by which method?
A. One round knockout   B. A draw
C. Twelve round points decision

778. In defence of his Commonwealth Bantamweight title Johnny Armour stopped challenger Rufus Adebayo in which round?
A. Five B. Six C. Seven

779. In defence of his WBO Penta-Continental Light-Heavyweight title Garry Delaney stopped Jim Murray in which round?
A. Five B. Six C. Seven

780. Juan John Molina retained his IBF Super-Featherweight title against Floyd Havard when he forced the challenger to retire in which round?
A. Five B. Six C. Seven

781. Where did the above contest take place?
A. Cardiff B. Glasgow C. London

782. How did Eamonn Loughran retain his WBO Welterweight crown against Alessandro Duran?
A. Two round stoppage B. Four round retirement
C. Twelve round points decision

783. Who was the referee of the above contest?
A. Ron Lipton B. Mills Lane C. John Coyle

784. Where did the above contest take place?
A. Belfast B. Glasgow C. London

785. Eamonn Loughran won the vacant WBO welterweight title when he defeated Lorenzo Smith by which method?
A. Two round stoppage B. Four round knockout
C. Twelve round points decision

786. Where did the above contest take place?
A. Ireland B. America C. France

787. In which round did Joe Calzaghe stop opponent Martin Rosamond on 22 January 1994?
A. One B. Two C. Three

788. In which round on 16 January 1994 did James Toney stop opponent Anthony Hembrick?
A. *Seven* B. *Eight* C. *Nine*

789. In which round did Lionel Butler knockout James "Bone Crusher" Smith on 18 January 1994?
A. *One* B. *Two* C. *Three*

790. Neville Brown retained his British Middleweight title on 26 January 1994 against Andrew Flute when the challenger retired in which round?
A. *Five* B. *Six* C. *Seven*

791. In defence of his WBO Light-Heavyweight crown Leonzer Barber stopped challenger Nicky Piper in which round?
A. *Nine* B. *Ten* C. *Eleven*

792. In which country was the above contest held?
A. *Britain* B. *America.* C. *France*

793. ***True or false,*** Nicky Piper is a member of MENSA?

794. Dennis Andries defeated Crawford Ashley on 29 January 1994 when he forced him to retire in which round?
A. *Three* B. *Four* C. *Five*

795. On 29 January 1994 Robbie Regan outpointed opponent Michele Poddighe over how many rounds?
A. *Six* B. *Eight* C. *Ten*

796. Where did the above contest take place?
A. *Cardiff* B. *London* C. *Manchester*

797. In a previous contest on 21 December 1990 Robbie Regan crossed gloves with Michele Poddighe with the result being a draw over how many rounds?
A. *Six* B. *Eight* C. *Ten*

798. Where did the above contest take place?
A. *England* B. *Wales* C. *Italy*

799. Duke McKenzie outpointed opponent Marcelo Rodriguez over how many rounds on 29 January 1994?
A. Six B. Eight C. Ten

800. In which round did Prince Naseem Hamed stop Peter Buckley on 29 January 1994?
A. Two B. Three C. Four

801. To win the vacant NABF Cruiserweight crown Thomas Hearns knocked out opponent Dan Ward in which round?
A. One B. Two C. Three

802. Simon Brown retained the WBC Light-Middleweight title against challenger Troy Waters by which method?
A. One round stoppage B. Four round knockout
C. Twelve round points decision

803. Frankie Randall won the WBC Light-Welterweight crown when he defeated holder Julio Cesar Chavez by which method?
A. Five round stoppage B. Nine round retirement
C. Twelve round points decision

804. *True or false,* Randall was the first man to defeat Chavez in the professional ranks?

805. Felix Trinidad retained his IBF Welterweight championship against challenger Hector Camacho by which method?
A. Three round stoppage B. Eight round knockout
C. Twelve round points decision

806. In which round did Giovanni Parisi stop opponent Mike Bryan on 29 January 1994?
A. One B. Two C. Three

807. In which round did Gary Mason stop opponent K.P. Porter?
A. One B. Two C. Three

808. In which country did the Mason - Porter contest take place?
A. England B. America C. Canada

809. How many contests did Don Cockell have during his professional career?
A. 79 B. 80 C. 81

810. *True or false,* former European and British Welterweight champion Peter Waterman once challenged for the world title?

811. To retain his WBA Light-Middleweight crown Julio Cesar Vasquez defeated Juan Medina Padilla by which method?
A. One round stoppage B. Nine round knockout
C. Twelve round points decision

812. In defence of his WBA Super-Featherweight crown Genaro Hernandez stopped Jorge Ramirez in which round?
A. Six B. Seven C. Eight

813. *True or false,* Larry Holmes boxed in Britain in 1994?

814. To win the European Cruiserweight title Carl Thompson knocked out defending champion Massimiliano Duran in which round?
A. Six B. Seven C. Eight

815. In which country did the above contest take place?
A. England B. France C. Italy

816. *True or false,* Massimiliano Duran was a former WBC world Cruiserweight champion.

817. In defence of his European welterweight crown Gary Jacobs defeated challenger Tek Nkalankete by which method?
A. One round stoppage B. Four round knockout
C. Twelve round points decision

818. Where did the above contest take place?
A. France B. Scotland C. Italy

819. Which was Henry Cooper awarded?
A. O.B.E. B. M.B.E. C. C.B.E.

820. In defence of his WBO Light-Flyweight title Josue Camacho defeated challenger Paul Weir by which method?
A. Two round stoppage B. Eight round knockout
C. Twelve round points decision

821. Was this Paul Weir's first defeat in the professional ranks?
Yes or no.

822. Where did the Camacho-Weir contest take place?
A. London B. Glasgow C. Cardiff

823. In defence of his European Bantamweight crown Vincenzo Belcastro defeated Drew Docherty by which method?
A. One round stoppage B. Nine round retirement
C. Twelve round points decision

824. Where did the above contest take place?
A. Italy B. Scotland C. Spain

825. In which round did Lonnie Beasley stop opponent Charles "The Hatchet" Brewer on 1 February 1994?
A. One B. Two C. Three

826. By which method did Chris Eubank retain his WBO world Super-Middleweight title against Graciano Rocchigiani?
A. One round stoppage B. A draw
C. Twelve round points decision

827. In which country did the above contest take place?
A. Italy B. England C. Germany

828. Graciano Rocchigiani was a former world Super-Middleweight champion. Which version of the title did he once hold?
A. IBF B. WBC C. WBA

829. At this stage of his career Chris Eubank was undefeated in how many contests?
A. 37 B. 38 C. 39

830. How many of Joe Frazier's professional bouts resulted in a draw?
A. One B. Two C. Three

831. To win the vacant Commonwealth Cruiserweight crown Franco Wanyama stopped Tony Booth in which round?
A. One B. Two C. Three

832. In defence of his WBO world Middleweight title Chris Pyatt knocked out challenger Mark Cameron in which round?
A. One B. Two C. Three

833. *True or false,* Pyatt took a count in the first round?

834. In which country did the above contest take place?
A. South Africa B. Germany C. England

835. Over how many rounds did Steve Collins outpoint Paul Wesley on 9 February 1994?
A. Six B. Eight C. Ten

836. In which round did Mark Tibbs stop opponent Kevin Toomey on 9 February 1994?
A. Two B. Three C. Four

837. In defence of his Commonwealth Flyweight title Darren Fifield stopped challenger Danny Porter in which round?
A. Six B. Seven C. Eight

838. Where did the above contest take place?
A. Bethnal Green B. Southwark. C. Mayfair

839. In defence of his IBF Featherweight crown Tom "Boom Boom" Johnson defeated Orlando Soto by which method?
A. One Round stoppage B. Two round knockout
C. Twelve round points decision

840. How did Jake Rodriguez win the IBF Light-Welterweight crown when challenging Charles Murray?
   A. Five round stoppage B. Eight round knockout
   C. Twelve round points decision

841. Where did the above contest take place?
   A. Las Vegas B. Atlantic City C. Los Angeles

842. In which round did Tommy Morrison knock out opponent Tui Toia on 20 February 1994?
   A. One B. Two C. Three

843. Robert McCracken won the British Light-Middleweight crown when he defeated holder Andy Till by which method?
   A. Two round knockout B. Ten round retirement
   C. Twelve round points decision

844. In defence of his WBC Super-Middleweight Title Nigel Benn defeated challenger Henry Wharton by which method?
   A. Three round retirement B. Eight round knockout
   C. Twelve round points decision

845. Where did the above contest take place?
   A. Manchester B. Earls Court C. Brentwood

846. This was Henry Wharton's first defeat in the professional ranks, *yes or no?*

847. In which round did Oliver McCall stop Dan Murphy on 26 February 1994?
   A. One B. Two C. Three

848. Steve Little won the WBA Super-Middleweight title when he defeated holder Michael Nunn by which method?
   A. Two round stoppage B. Five round knockout
   C. Twelve round points decision

849. In which country did the above contest take place?
   A. America B. England C. France

850. Michael Carruth made his professional debut by outpointing opponent George Wilson over how many rounds on 26 February 1994?
A. Four B. Six C. Eight

851. In which round did Adrian Dodson knockout Shamus Casey on 26 February 1994?
A. One B. Two C. Three

852. Dennis Andries outpointed opponent Mike Peak over how many rounds on 26 February 1994?
A. Four B. Six C. Eight

853. In defence of his Commonwealth Light-Middleweight crown Lloyd Honeyghan stopped challenger Kevin Adamson in which round?
A. Five B. Six C. Seven

854. In defence of his IBF Bantamweight crown Orlando Canizales stopped Gerardo Martinez in which round?
A. Three B. Four C. Five

855. In which round did Richie Woodhall stop opponent Heath Todd on 1 March 1994?
A. Seven B. Eight C. Nine

856. At this stage, Richie Woodhall was now undefeated in how many professional contests?
A. 14 B. 15 C. 16

857. Joe Calzaghe stopped opponent Darren Littlewood in which round on 1 March 1994?
A. One B. Two C. Three

858. Oscar De La Hoya won the WBO Super-Featherweight title when holder Jimmy Bredahl retired in which round?
A. Nine B. Ten C. Eleven

859. Where did the above contest take place?
A. Atlantic City B. Las Vegas C. Los Angeles

860. Oscar De La Hoya was now undefeated in how many contests?
A. 12 B. 13 C. 14

861. In defence of his IBF Super-Middleweight crown James Toney stopped challenger Tim Littles in which round?
A. Four B. Five C. Six

862. Where did the above contest take place?
A. Atlantic City B. Las Vegas C. Los Angeles

863. How did Gianfranco Rosi retain his IBF Light-Middleweight crown against challenger Vincent Pettway on 4 March 1994?
A. One round knockout B. Four round retirement.
C. Six round technical draw

864. In which country did the above contest take place?
A. Italy B. America C. France

865. By which method did Orlin Norris retain his WBA Cruiserweight title against challenger Arthur Williams on the 4 March 1994?
A. Two round stoppage B. Eight round knockout
C. Twelve round points decision

866. Where did the above contest take place?
A. Atlantic City B. Las Vegas C. New Orleans

867. In defence of his WBC Middleweight title Gerald McClellan stopped Gilbert Baptist in which round?
A. One B. Two C. Three

868. Where did the above contest take place?
A. Las Vegas B. Mexico City C. Boston

869. Over how many rounds did Julian Jackson outpoint Eduardo Ayala in 1994?
A. Six B. Eight C. Ten

870. In defence of his WBA Light-Middleweight championship Julio Cesar Vasquez stopped challenger Armand Picar in which round?
A. One B. Two C. Three

871. Where did the above contest take place?
A. New Orleans B. Inglewood C. Las Vegas

872. Over how many rounds did Carlos De Leon outpoint opponent Bobby Joe Arthurs on 17 February 1994?
A. Six B. Eight C. Ten

873. In defence of his South African Light-Heavyweight title Sugarboy Malinga knocked out challenger Mohammed Isaacs in which round?
A. Five B. Six C. Seven

874. In defence of his WBO world Featherweight title Steve Robinson knocked out Paul Hodkinson in which round?
A. Ten B. Eleven C. Twelve

875. *True or false,* Robinson was down for a count in round three?

876. Where did the Robinson-Hodkinson contest take place?
A. Cardiff B. Llanelli C. Barry

877. Robbie Regan outpointed opponent Mauricio Bernal over how many rounds on 12 March 1994?
A. Six B. Eight C. Ten

878. At this stage of his career Robbie Regan had taken part in how many professional contests?
A. 15 B. 16 C. 17

879. To win the British Super-Middleweight title Cornelius Carr defeated holder James Cook by which method?
A. One round stoppage B. Six round knockout
C. Twelve round points decision

880. Over how many rounds did Larry Holmes outpoint Garing Lane on 8 March 1994?
A. Six B. Eight C. Ten

881. In which round did Frank Bruno stop opponent Jesse Ferguson on 16 March 1994?
A. One B. Two C. Three

882. Over how many rounds did Neville Brown outpoint Wallid Underwood on 16 March 1994?
A. Six B. Eight C. Ten

883. In which round did Richie Woodhall stop opponent Greg Lonon on 16 March 1994?
A. Four B. Five C. Six

884. To win the WBO world Heavyweight title Herbie Hide knocked out holder Michael Bentt in which round?
A. Seven B. Eight C. Nine

885. *True or false,* Hide was down for a count in round four?

886. In which country did the Bentt-Hide contest take place?
A. America B. England C. France

887. At this stage of his career Herbie Hide was undefeated in how many professional contests?
A. 26 B. 27 C. 28

888. In defence of his WBA Light-Welterweight title Juan Martin -Coggi stopped challenger Eder Gonzalez in which round on 18 March 1994?
A. One B. Two C. Three

889. Where did the above contest take place?
A. Las Vegas B. St.Louis C. Los Angeles

890. *True or false,* prior to winning the WBO Heavyweight crown Herbie Hide was a former European title holder?

891. In defence of his WBA Super-Bantamweight title Wilfredo Vasquez stopped challenger Yuichi Kasai in which round?
A. One B. Two C. Three

892. In which country did the above contest take place?
A. Mexico B. America C. Japan

893. In defence of his WBA Lightweight title on 19 March 1994 Orzubek Nazarov defeated challenger Dingaan Thobela by which method?
A. One round stoppage B. Five round knockout
C. Twelve round points decision

894. When Jess Willard knocked out Jack Johnson in round 26 on 5 April 1915 he became at that time the tallest man to win the world Heavyweight crown. How tall was he?
A. 6ft. 3 inches B. 6ft. 5 inches C. 6ft. 6¼ inches

895. In which weight division was Miguel Velasquez a WBC world champion?
A. Lightweight B. Light-welterweight
C. Welterweight

896. Which British title did Pat Thomas **not** hold during his career?
A. Welterweight B. Light-Middleweight
C. Middleweight

897. The film "Raging Bull" was based on which former world Middleweight champion?
A. Tony Zale B. Jake La Motta C. Rocky Graziano

898. Solly Kreiger won a version of a world title in which weight division?
A. Middleweight B. Light-Heavyweight C. Heavyweight

899. Floyd Havard won the British Super-Featherweight crown when he stopped holder Neil Haddock in which round?
A. Nine B. Ten C. Eleven

900. Where did the Havard v Haddock title contest take place?
     A. Belfast   B. Glasgow   C. Cardiff

901. Floyd Havard was a former holder of the British Super Featherweight crown. Who did he defeat in 1988 to win the title?
     A. Pat Cowdell   B. Najib Daho   C. John Doherty

902. By which method did he win the crown?
     A. Stoppage in round eight   B. Knockout in round ten
     C. Twelve round points decision

903. Dennis Andries failed to win the vacant WBC international Cruiserweight title when he was defeated by Przemyslaw "Chemek" Saleta by which method?
     A. Four round stoppage   B. Ten round knockout
     C. Twelve round points decision

904. How tall is Henry Akinwande?
     A. 6ft. 5 inches   B. 6ft. 6 inches   C. 6ft. 7 inches

905. Henry Maske retained his IBF Light-heavyweight title when he stopped challenger Ernie Magdaleno in which round?
     A. Nine   B. Ten   C. Eleven

906. In which round did Roy Jones stop opponent Danny Garcia on 22 March 1994?
     A. Six   B. Seven.   C. Eight

907. In defence of his WBO Super-Flyweight title on 25 March 1994, how did Johnny Bredahl defeat Eduardo Nazario?
     A. Three Round stoppage   B. Eight Round Knockout
     C. Twelve Round points decision

908. In which round did Mark Tibbs stop opponent George Wilson on 29 March 1994?
     A. Four   B. Five   C. Six

909. In which round did Tommy Morrison stop opponent Bryan "Boom Boom" Scott on 29 March 1994?
   A. One B. Two C. Three

910. Which boxer is nick-named Hoko?
   A. Steve Robinson B. Paul Hodkinson
   C. Colin McMillan

911. In defence of his WBC Lightweight crown Miguel Angel Gonzalez stopped Jean-Baptiste Mendy in which round?
   A. Three B. Four C. Five

912. In which country did the above contest take place?
   A. America B. France C. Mexico

913. In which round did Prince Naseem Hamed knockout opponent John Miceli on 9 April 1994?
   A. One B. Two C. Three

914. In defence of his WBO Penta-Continental Light-Heavyweight crown Garry Delaney knocked out challenger Simon Harris in which round?
   A. Four B. Five C. Six

915. Delaney and Harris had crossed gloves previously in an eight round contest which took place in 1992. What was the result on that occasion?
   A. Eight round points win for Harris
   B. Points win for Delaney C. A draw

916. In defence of his WBC welterweight title how did Pernell Whitaker retain his crown against Santos Cardona?
   A. Five round stoppage B. Nine round knockout.
   C. Twelve Round points decision

917. In defence of his WBC Super-Bantamweight title, how did Tracy Harris Patterson defeat Richard Duran?
   A. Five round stoppage B. Seven round retirement
   C. Twelve round points decision

918. Where did the above contest take place?
   A. Reno B. New York C. Atlantic City

919. Whose middle name is Livingstone?
   A. Nigel Benn B. Roy Jones C. Chris Eubank

920. In defence of his European Welterweight title Gary Jacobs knocked out challenger Alessandro Duran in which round?
   A. Seven B. Eight C. Nine

921. In which round did Johnny Tapia stop opponent Arturo Estrada on 15 April 1994?
   A. One B. Two C. Three

922. To win the vacant European Lightweight title Racheed Lawal knocked out Paul Burke in which round?
   A. Two B. Three C. Four

923. In defence of his IBF Light-Welterweight title Jake Rodriguez defeated Ray Oliveira by which method?
   A. Eight round stoppage B. Ten round knockout
   C. Twelve round points decision

924. To win the WBA Bantamweight title John Michael Johnson stopped Holder Junior Jones in which round?
   A. Nine B. Ten C. Eleven

925. Where did the above contest take place?
   A. New York B. Reno C. Las Vegas

926. To win the WBA and IBF versions of the world Heavyweight title, how did Michael Moorer defeat holder Evander Holyfield?
   A. Three round stoppage B. Eight round knockout
   C. Twelve round points decision

927. Who was the referee of the above contest?
   A. Mills Lane B. Arthur Mercante Snr.
   C. Frank Cappuccino

928. Where did the above contest take place?
   A. Atlantic City   B. Las Vegas   C. Reno

929. Michael Moorer was now undefeated in how many professional contests?
   A. 35   B. 36   C. 37

930. Juan Molina retained his IBF Super-Featherweight title against Gregorio "Goyo" Vargas by which method?
   A. One round stoppage   B. Three round knockout.
   C. Twelve round points decision

931. Who was the referee of the above contest?
   A. Mills Lane   B. Toby Gibson   C. Joe Cortez

932. To win the inaugural British Super-Bantamweight crown Richie Wenton stopped Bradley Stone in which round?
   A. Nine   B. Ten   C. Eleven

933. Luigi Camputaro retained his European Flyweight title against challenger Mickey Cantwell by which method?
   A. Eight round stoppage   B. Ten round knockout
   C. Twelve Round points decision

934. Where did the above contest take place?
   A. Italy   B. France   C. England

935. In defence of his IBF Super-Flyweight title Julio Ccsar Borboa stopped Jorge Luis Roman in which round?
   A. Two   B. Three   C. Four

936. In defence of his WBC world Heavyweight title Lennox Lewis stopped challenger Phil Jackson in which round?
   A. Six   B. Seven   C. Eight

937. Who was the referee of the above contest?
   A. Arthur Mercante Snr.   B. Mills Lane   C. Rudy Battle

938. In which country did the above contest take place?
   A. England   B. America   C. France

939. Lennox Lewis was now undefeated in how many professional contests?
A. 25 B. 26 C. 27

940. To win the vacant WBC international Heavyweight title James Oyebola knocked out Scott Welch in which round?
A. Three B. Four C. Five

941. In which country did the above contest take place?
A. America B. England C. Italy

942. How tall is James Oyebola?
A. 6ft. 7 inches B. 6ft. 8 inches C. 6ft. 9 inches

943. In defence of his WBC Featherweight title Kevin Kelley defeated challenger Jesse Benavides by which method?
A. One round stoppage B. Two round knockout
C. Twelve round points decision

944. To regain his WBC Light-Middleweight crown Terry Norris defeated holder Simon Brown by which method?
A. Two round stoppage B. Eleven round knockout
C. Twelve round points decision

945. Julio Cesar Chavez regained his WBC Light-welterweight crown from holder Frankie Randall by which method?
A. Two round stoppage B. Five round retirement
C. Eight Round technical points decision

946. In defence of his WBC Middleweight crown on 7 May 1994, Gerald McClellan knocked out Julian Jackson in which round?
A. One B. Two C. Three

947. To win the WBC Super-Featherweight crown Jesse James Leija defeated holder Azumah Nelson by which method?
A. Five round stoppage B. Nine round knockout
C. Twelve round points decision

948. In defence of his WBC Strawweight crown Ricardo Lopez defeated challenger Kermin Guardia by which method?
A. One round stoppage B. Nine round knockout
C. Twelve round points decision

949. To win the WBO world Middleweight crown Steve Collins stopped holder Chris Pyatt in which round?
A. Three B. Four C. Five

950. Who was the referee of the above contest?
A. Paul Thomas B. John Coyle C. Dave Parris

951. In which round did Clifton Mitchell stop Emanuel Brites Camargo on 11 May 1994?
A. One B. Two C. Three

952. To win the European Bantamweight title, how did Prince Naseem Hamed defeat holder Vincenzo Belcastro?
A. One round stoppage B. Eight round retirement
C. Twelve round points decision

953. In which country did the above contest take place?
A. Italy B. England C. Spain

954. In defence of his Commonwealth Lightweight title Billy Schwer stopped challenger Howard Grant in which round?
A. Seven B. Eight C. Nine

955. Who was the refcree of the above contest?
A. John Coyle B. Mickey Vann C. Paul Thomas

956. In which country did the above contest take place?
A. Canada B. England C. Australia

957. In defence of his IBF Super-Flyweight crown Julio Cesar Borboa stopped challenger Jaji Sibali in which round?
A. Nine B. Ten C. Eleven

958. To win the WBC Super-Flyweight championship, how did Hiroshi Kawashima defeat holder Jose Luis Bueno?
A. Two round stoppage   B. Eight round knockout
C. Twelve round points decision

959. In which country did the above contest take place?
A. Argentina   B. America   C. Japan

960. In defence of his IBF Strawweight title Ratanapol Sowvoraphin stopped Roger Espanola in which round?
A. Four   B. Five   C. Six

961. In which country did the above contest take place?
A. Thailand   B. Japan   C. America

962. How did Chris Eubank retain his WBO Super-Middleweight crown against challenger Ray Close on 21 May 1994?
A. Three round stoppage   B. Eight round knockout
C. Twelve round points decision

963. Where did the above contest take place?
A. Cardiff   B. Glasgow   C. Belfast

964. In defence of his WBA Light-Middleweight title Julio Cesar Vasquez stopped Ahmet Dottuev in which round?
A. Ten   B. Eleven   C. Twelve

965. Who was the referee of the above contest?
A. Mickey Vann   B. John Coyle   C. Dave Parris

966. Where did the above contest take place?
A. Argentina   B. Ireland   C. Germany

967. What is the nationality of Ahmet Dottuev?
A. German   B. Russian   C. French

968. Over how many rounds did Sam Storey outpoint Fidel Castro Smith in their contest on 21 May 1994?
A. Six   B. Eight   C. Ten

969. In which round did Clifton Mitchell knockout opponent Steve Garber on 21 May 1994?
A. One B. Two C. Three

970. How many world Heavyweight title contests did Tommy Burns have during his professional career?
A. Eleven B. Twelve C. Thirteen

971. Over how many rounds did Johnny Tapia outpoint opponent Antonio Ruiz in their 1994 contest?
A. Six B. Eight C. Ten

972. To win the British and Commonwealth Light-Welterweight titles Ross Hale stopped holder Andy Holligan in which round?
A. One B. Two C. Three

973. Who was the referee of the above contest?
A. John Coyle B. Dave Parris C. Mickey Vann

974. Billy Hardy defended his Commonwealth title and won the vacant British Featherweight title when he stopped Alan McKay in which round?
A. Seven B. Eight C. Nine

975. *True or false,* Billy Hardy was down for two counts in round one?

976. In their contest on 24 May 1994 Michael Ayers and Karl Taylor boxed over eight rounds. What was the result?
A. Points win for Ayers B. Points win for Taylor
C. A draw

977. *True or false,* in a previous contest Ayers stopped Taylor in the first round?

978. In defence of his WBO Super-Featherweight title Oscar De La Hoya stopped Giorgio Campanella in which round?
A. One B. Two C. Three

979. Who was the referee of the above contest?
   A. Mills Lane B. Rudy Battle C. Joe Cortez

980. Where did the above contest take place?
   A. Las Vegas B. New York C. Atlantic City

981. In defence of his IBF Middleweight crown Roy Jones stopped challenger Thomas Tate in which round?
   A. One B. Two C. Three

982. Who was the referee of the above contest?
   A. Joe Cortez B. Mills Lane C. Richard Steele

983. Where did the above contest take place ?
   A. Las Vegas B. Atlantic City C. New York

984. *True or false,* Roy Jones took two counts in the first round?

985. *True or false,* Thomas Tate is the Brother of former IBF world Middleweight champion Frank Tate?

986. In which Weight Division was Marvin Hart a world champion?
   A. Middleweight B. Light-Heavyweight C. Heavyweight

987. In defence of his IBF Lightweight crown Rafael Ruelas stopped challenger Mike Evgen in which round?
   A. One B. Two C. Three

988. Where did the above contest take place?
   A. Las Vegas B. Atlantic City C. San Francisco

989. In defence of his WBO Featherweight crown Steve Robinson defeated Freddy Cruz by which method?
   A. Four round stoppage B. Eight round knockout
   C. Twelve round points decision

990. Who was the referee of the above contest?
   A. Richard Steele B. Toby Gibson C. Mills Lane

991. Where did the above contest take place?
A. Swansea B. Cardiff C. Llanelli

992. In which round did Robin Reid stop opponent Andy Furlong on 4 June 1994?
A. One B. Two C. Three

993. In which round did Joe Calzaghe stop Karl Barwise on 4 June 1994?
A. One B. Two C. Three

994. To win the WBA Welterweight championship Ike "Bazooka" Quartey stopped holder Crisanto Espana in which round?
A. Ten B. Eleven C. Twelve

995. Over how many rounds did James Toney outpoint opponent Vinson Durham on 18 May 1994?
A. Six B. Eight C. Ten

996. In defence of his IBF world Light-Heavyweight title Henry Maske defeated challenger Andrea Magi by which method?
A. Five round stoppage B. Nine round knockout
C. Twelve round points decision

997. Who was the referee the above contest?
A. Robert Gonzales B. Toby Gibson C. Mitch Halpern

998. Where did the above contest take place?
A. Berlin B. Munich C. Dortmund

999. In defence of his WBO Flyweight title Baby Jake Matlala defeated Francis Ampofo when he retired in which round?
A. Seven B. Eight C. Nine

1000. Who was the referee of the above contest?
A. Raul Caiz B. Laurence Cole C. Toby Gibson

1001. In which country did the above contest take place?
A. South Africa B. England C. France

ROUND ELEVEN

1002. In defence of his IBF Bantamweight title Orlando Canizales knocked out challenger Rolando Bohol in which round?
A. Three B. Four C. Five

1003. Who was the referee of the above contest?
A. Mills Lane B. Laurence Cole C. Richard Steele

1004. To win the vacant USBA Bantamweight title Mario Diaz defeated opponent Eddie Rangel by which method?
A. Five round stoppage B. Nine round knockout
C. Twelve round points decision

1005. In defence of his IBF Featherweight title Tom "Boom Boom" Johnson stopped Benny Amparo in which round?
A. Ten B. Eleven C. Twelve

1006. Where did the above contest take place?
A. Atlantic City B. Las Vegas C. Inglewood

1007. In defence of his WBA Flyweight crown Saen Sorploenchit defeated challenger Aquiles Guzman by which method?
A. Two round stoppage B. Eight round knockout
C. Twelve round points decision

1008. Where did the above contest take place?
A. Japan B. Korea C. Thailand

1009. In which year did Charlie Magri win the ABA Light-Flyweight title?
A. 1973 B. 1974 C. 1975

1010. In defence of his European Cruiserweight crown Carl Thompson knocked out Akim Tafer in which round?
A. Six B. Seven C. Eight

1011. In which country did the above contest take place?
A. France B. England C. Italy

1012. Over how many rounds did Vinny Pazienza outpoint Roberto Duran on 25 June 1994?
A. Eight B. Ten C. Twelve

1013. Who was the referee of the above contest?.
A. Joe Cortez B. Toby Gibson C. Richard Steele

1014. In which round did Jorge Luis Gonzalez knockout Mike Evans on 24 June 1994?
A. One B. Two C. Three

1015. In which round did Johnny Tapia stop Rafael Granillo on 24 June 1994?
A. Seven B. Eight C. Nine

1016. In defence of his WBA Cruiserweight crown Orlin Norris knocked out challenger Arthur Williams in which round?
A. One B. Two C. Three

1017. Who was the referee of the above contest?.
A. Richard Steele B. Mills Lane C. Joe Cortez

1018. Where did the above contest take place?.
A. Las Vegas B. Atlantic City C. Boston

1019. On which date in 1994 did this bout take place.?
A. 2 July B. 3 July C. 4 July

1020. In defence of his WBA Super-Bantamweight crown Wilfredo Vasquez stopped Jae-Won Choi in which round?
A. One B. Two C. Three

1021. Who was the referee of the above contest?.
A. John Coyle B. Mitch Halpern C. Mills Lane

1022. In which country did the above contest take place?
A. America B. Korea C. France

1023. Did Frank Bruno win a Gold medal at the Commonwealth games during his amateur career, *yes or no?*

1024. In which round did Tony Tucker stop opponent Cecil Coffee on 2 July 1994?
A. One *B. Two* *C. Three*

1025. In which round did Bruce Seldon stop Tui Toia on 2 July 1994?
A. One *B. Two* *C. Three*

1026. In defence of his WBO Super-Bantamweight crown Daniel Jimenez defeated Cristobal Pasqual by which method?
A. One round stoppage *B. Two round knockout*
C. Twelve round points decision

1027. Leo Gamez retained his WBA Light-Flyweight crown against Kaj Ratchabandit by which method?
A. Two round stoppage *B. A draw*
C. Twelve round points decision

1028. Where did the above contest take place?.
A. America *B. Japan* *C. Thailand*

1029. How did Hector Camacho defeat Craig Snyder on 9 June 1994?
A. Two round stoppage *B. Three round knockout*
C. Ten round point decision

1030. In defence of his WBO Super-Middleweight title Chris Eubank defeated Mauricio Amaral by which method?
A. Two round stoppage *B. Eight round retirement*
C. Twelve round points decision

1031. In which country did the above contest take place?.
A. Germany *B. France* *C. England*

1032. In defence of his WBO Penta-Continental Light-Heavyweight crown how did Garry Delaney defeat Sergio Merani?
A. Four round stoppage *B. Nine round knockout.*
C. Twelve round points decision

1033. Over how many rounds did Drew Docherty outpoint opponent Conn McMullen on 9 July 1994?
A. Six B. Eight C. Ten

1034. In which round did Mark Delaney knockout Eddie Knight on 9 July 1994?
A. Two B. Three C. Four

1035. To win the WBO Light-Flyweight crown Michael Carbajal defeated holder Josue Camacho by which method?
A. Three round stoppage B. Nine round knockout.
C. Twelve round points decision

1036. Where did the above contest take place?.
A. Laredo B. Phoenix C. San Francisco

1037. Anaclet Wamba retained his WBC Cruiserweight crown against challenger Adolpho Washington on 14 July 1994 by which method?
A. One round stoppage B. Nine round knockout.
C. Twelve round draw

1038. Who was the referee of the above contest?
A. Dave Parris B. Mickey Vann C. John Coyle

1039. To win the WBA Bantamweight title Daorung Chuwatana (MP Petroleum) stopped holder John Michael Johnson in which round?
A. One B. Two C. Three

1040. In which country did the above contest take place?.
A. America B. Thailand C. Italy

1041. In defence of his European Heavyweight title Henry Akinwande knocked out challenger Mario Schiesser in which round?
A. Six. B. Seven C. Eight

1042. In which country did the above contest take place?
A. Germany B. Italy C. England

1043. In which round did Dave Anderson knockout opponent John Stovin on 21 July 1994?
A. Three B. Four C. Five

1044. In defence of his European Middleweight crown Agostino Cardamone stopped Neville Brown in which round?
A. Five B. Six C. Seven

1045. In which country did the above contest take place?.
A. England B. Italy C. Spain

1046. To win the WBC Light-Heavyweight title Mike McCallum defeated holder Jeff Hardin by which method?
A. Two round stoppage B. Ten round knockout
C. Twelve round points decision

1047. To retain his WBA Light-Heavyweight crown Virgil Hill defeated challenger Frank Tate by which method?
A. One round stoppage B. Three round knockout
C. Twelve round points decision

1048. In defence of his IBF Cruiserweight title Alfred "Ice" Cole defeated challenger Nate Miller by which method?
A. Eight round stoppage B. Nine round knockout
C. Twelve round points decision

1049. In which round did Dean Francis stop opponent Horace Fleary on 21 July 1994?
A. Two B. Three C. Four

1050. To win the WBO world Bantamweight title Alfred "Cobra" Kotey defeated holder Rafael Del Valle by which method?
A. One round stoppage B. Five round retirement
C. Twelve round points decision

1051. Who was the referee of the above contest?.
A. John Coyle B. Dave Parris C. Mickey Vann

1052.   In defence of his Commonwealth Super-Featherweight title
        Tony Pep stopped challenger J.T. Williams in which round?
        A. One B. Two C. Three

1053.   Who was the referee of the above contest?.
        A. Mickey Vann B. John Coyle C. Dave Parris

1054.   In defence of his IBF Super-Middleweight crown James
        Toney knocked out challenger Prince Charles Williams in
        which round?
        A. Ten B. Eleven C. Twelve

1055.   Who was the referee of the above contest?
        A. Jay Nady B. Joe Cortez C. Mills Lane

1056.   Where did the above contest take place?.
        A. Las Vegas B. Atlantic City C. San Francisco

1057.   To win the vacant WBO Lightweight title Oscar De La
        Hoya knocked out opponent Jorge "Maromero" Paez in
        which round?
        A. One B. Two C. Three

The Championship Quiz   Answers

1. Two
2. Curtis Ramsey
3. Nick Wilshire
4. Fifteen round points decision
5. True
6. Light-Heavyweight
7. Matt Franklin
8. No
9. New York
10. Hugo Corro
11. Light-Middleweight
12. Walter McGowan
13. Six
14. Sean Mannion
15. New York
16. False
17. True
18. Selvin Bell
19. No
20. Gold
21. Six
22. Neville Meade
23. Ten
24. New York
25. One
26. Italy
27. Once
28. Super-Featherweight
29. Eusebio Pedroza
30. Antonio Cervantes
31. Kirkland Laing
32. Twice
33. No
34. WBC
35. Charlie Magri
36. Once
37. Bruce Curry
38. Commonwealth
39. A Twelve round Draw
40. Vito Antuofermo
41. Middleweight
42. No
43. Twice
44. Light-Middleweight
45. Howard Winstone
46. No
47. Featherweight
48. Bernd August
49. True
50. Once
51. Gary Summerhays
52. Cliff Gilpin
53. Australia
54. Six
55. Two
56. Las Vegas
57. Cruiserweight
58. South Africa
59. Jimmy Cable
60. No
61. Gene Hatcher
62. Light-Middleweight
63. James "Bonecrusher" Smith
64. Cruiser
65. Lorenzo Garcia
66. Floyd Patterson and Floyd Havard - the other being John Conteh

67 .	Phil Brown	100 .	Two
68 .	Denmark	101 .	Bronze
69 .	Two	102 .	Chicago
70 .	WBC	103 .	Cruiserweight
71 .	True	104 .	A points win for Brown
72 .	No	105 .	Hughroy Currie
73 .	Ciro De Leva	106 .	Ireland
74 .	Italy	107 .	Sam Reeson
75 .	True	108 .	Nine
76 .	Twelve round points decision	109 .	Three
		110 .	Sunderland
77 .	Cliff Gilpin	111 .	Super-Featherweight
78 .	World	112 .	True
79 .	One	113 .	1985
80 .	One	114 .	Italy
81 .	World	115 .	Nine
82 .	Texas	116 .	1989
83 .	Six	117 .	Twelve round points decision
84 .	Three times		
85 .	No	118 .	One
86 .	Germany	119 .	Five
87 .	A Draw	120 .	America
88 .	Miguel Cebrero	121 .	Nine
89 .	Lightweight	122 .	Nine
90 .	Fourteen times	123 .	Las Vegas
91 .	Stewart Lithgo	124 .	One
92 .	IBF	125 .	Four
93 .	Clemente Tshinza	126 .	England
94 .	France	127 .	Eight
95 .	No	128 .	Middleweight
96 .	False	129 .	No
97 .	Twelve round points decision	130 .	False
		131 .	1985
98 .	One	132 .	25
		133 .	Spain
		134 .	One
ROUND TWO		135 .	America
		136 .	Nine
99 .	Reno		

137 . Seven
138 . 1989
139 . Outpointed over twelve rounds
140 . 1989
141 . Adrian Morgan
142 . Eight
143 . Twelve round points decision
144 . John Coyle
145 . Seven
146 . One
147 . Jorge Amparo
148 . Twelve
149 . Joe Cortez
150 . England
151 . Yes
152 . 1989
153 . Eight
154 . Larry Rozadilla
155 . Six
156 . Six
157 . 1989
158 . Patrick Lumumba
159 . Twelve round points decision
160 . Yes
161 . England
162 . 1989
163 . False
164 . Twelve round points decision
165 . Nine
166 . Larry O' Connell
167 . Eight
168 . Outpointed over six rounds
169 . True

170 . Twelve round points decision
171 . England
172 . America
173 . Six
174 . One
175 . England
176 . Twelve round points decision
177 . France
178 . Seven
179 . A five round stoppage for Patterson
180 . Ten round points decision
181 . Ten
182 . Ten round points decision
183 . No
184 . Ten
185 . Octavio Meyran
186 . Japan
187 . Eleven
188 . Twelve round points decision
189 . False
190 . Four
191 . Adrian Morgan
192 . True
193 . Twelve round points decision
194 . Twelve round points decision
195 . One
196 . False
197 . Eleven

ROUND THREE

198 . Roberto Ramirez
199 . England
200 . One
201 . Marlon Starling
202 . Eight
203 . Randy Neumann
204 . Atlantic City
205 . One
206. Twelve round points
decision
207 . Three
208 . False
209 . Six round draw
210 . Twelve round points
decision
211 . Eight
212 . Eleven
213 . Knockout In round four
214 . Light-Heavy
215 . Two
216 . Stopped In round Three
217 . True
218 . Twelve
219 . Four
220 . Four
221 . No
222 . Seven
223 . Australia
224 . True
225 . Twelve round points
decision
226 . Italy
227 . One
228 . One
229 . America
230 . Six

231 . 1989
232 . Six
233 . Serg Fame
234 . 1987
235 . Eyup Can
236 . Five
237 . Three
238 . Ten
239 . Belfast
240 . Middle
241 . One
242 . True
243 . No
244 . Three
245 . Nine
246 . Twelve round points
decision
247 . Thailand
248 . Ten round points
decision
249 . Cardiff
250 . Seven
251 . Ten round points
decision
252 . False
253 . True
254 . One
255 . Three
256 . Ten
257 . One
258 . 1991
259 . Eleven
260 . No
261 . Two
262 . False
263 . Jorge Vaca
264 . Twelve round points
decision

265 .	South Wales	293 .	True
266 .	Smokin Joe	294 .	Twelve round Draw
267 .	Twelve	295 .	Twelve round points decision
268 .	Tottenham		
269 .	Twelve round points decision	296 .	England
		297 .	Twelve round points decision
270 .	Twelve round points decision		
		298 .	Scotland
271 .	England	299 .	False
272 .	1992	300 .	Twelve round points decision
273 .	Twelve round points decision		
		301 .	One
274 .	False	302 .	One
275 .	One	303 .	1987
276 .	Ten round points decision		

ROUND FOUR

277 .	Eleven		
278 .	True	304 .	Three
279 .	True	305 .	Ireland
280 .	Twelve round points decision	306 .	WBA
		307 .	Stopped In Twelve
281 .	Twelve round points decision	308 .	England
		309 .	Eight
282 .	Glasgow	310 .	Twelve round points decision
283 .	Twelve round points decision		
		311 .	England
284 .	Three	312 .	Four
285 .	Ten round points decision	313 .	Five
		314 .	True
286 .	America	315 .	Twelve round points decision
287 .	Twelve		
288 .	Yes	316 .	America
289 .	Twelve round points decision	317 .	WBC
		318 .	Twelve round Draw
290 .	Twelve round points decision	319 .	England
		320 .	Nigel Benn
291 .	England	321 .	Five
292 .	Two	322 .	Scotland

323 .	Twelve round points decision	356 .	Twelve round points decision
324 .	Spain	357 .	England
325 .	Twelve round points decision	358 .	Six
		359 .	London
326 .	Mills Lane	360 .	Three
327 .	Las Vegas	361 .	Eight
328 .	False	362 .	Two
329 .	1992	363 .	England
330 .	Twelve round points decision	364 .	Twelve round points decision
331 .	Twelve round points decision	365 .	South Wales
		366 .	Twelve round points decision
332 .	Ten		
333 .	France	367 .	Las Vegas
334 .	Super-Bantamweight	368 .	Joe Cortez
335 .	Points win for Canizales	369 .	True
336 .	Twelve round points decision	370 .	Eleven
		371 .	Twelve round points decision
337 .	Glasgow	372 .	Twelve round points decision
338 .	America		
339 .	Eight	373 .	Cardiff
340 .	England	374 .	Five
341 .	1969	375 .	Floyd Patterson
342 .	Ricky Beard	376 .	1960
343 .	Two	377 .	Four
344 .	1992	378 .	England
345 .	Eduardo Vallejo	379 .	Points win for Proto
346 .	Two	380 .	France
347 .	Glasgow	381 .	1986
348 .	One	382 .	Muhammad Ali
349.	Three	383 .	Ludovic Proto
350 .	Ten	384 .	France
351 .	One	385 .	One
352 .	Three	386 .	Joe Santarpia
353 .	Italy	387 .	New York
354 .	False	388 .	WBA
355 .	Two		

389.	Six	421.	Ten
390.	One	422.	Six
391.	True	423.	True
392.	Four	424.	Ten
393.	Seven	425.	America
394.	England	426.	True
395.	Twelve round points decision	427.	Eleven
		428.	Three
396.	England	429.	Four
		430.	Silver

ROUND FIVE

		431.	One
		432.	Eight
397.	Ten	433.	One
398.	Herbie Hide	434.	Three
399.	Tommy Burns	435.	France
400.	Five	436.	One
401.	122	437.	Nine
402.	1970	438.	Three
403.	1987	439.	Nine
404.	Fourteen	440.	Swansea
405.	1987	441.	1993
406.	Glyn Rhodes	442.	Bronze
407.	Six	443.	Mark Dawson
408.	Honeyghan retired in round Ten	444.	One
		445.	Eight
409.	Argentinean	446.	Five
410.	Eight	447.	Seven
411.	Japan	448.	Twelve round points decision
412.	Thirteen		
413.	Primo Carnera	449.	Twelve round points decision
414.	Four		
415.	Spain	450.	False
416.	Yes	451.	Four
417.	WBA	452.	Ten round points decision
418.	England		
419.	Featherweight	453.	Points victory for Parisi
420.	Twelve round points decision	454.	Italy
		455.	One

456. True	488. Glasgow
457. Seven	489. Eight
458. Ten	490. Glasgow
459. Twelve round points decision	491. Seven
	492. Six
460. Three	493. True
461. Ten	494. Five
462. England	495. Nine
463. Six	496. Twelve round points decision
464. America	
465. False	497. Twelve round points decision
466. Eight	
467. Twelve round points decision	498. England
	499. Twelve round points decision
468. Seven	
469. Dublin	500. False
470. Eight	501. England
471. Nine	
472. Robin Reid	**ROUND SIX**
473. Eleven	
474. Australia	502. Twelve round points decision
475. Twelve round draw	
476. Germany	503. Two
477. Twelve round points decision	504. Two
	505. Twelve round points decision
478. Ten	
479. Twelve round points decision	506. One
	507. Twelve round points decision
480. Three	
481. Six	508. Las Vegas
482. Twelve round points decision	509. 1963
	510. European
483. IBF	511. Ten
484. Five	512. Twelve round points decision
485. Twelve round points decision	
	513. Ten
486. Four	514. Thirteen
487. Twelve round draw	

515.	Twelve round points decision	550.	Seven
516.	1967	551.	Las Vegas
517.	Eight	552.	Twelve round points decision
518.	Japan	553.	Twelve round points decision
519.	Three		
520.	San Diego	554.	1958
521.	True	555.	Joe Louis
522.	Two	556.	Seven
523.	Twenty	557.	Oldham
524.	Four	558.	Six
525.	False	559.	1992
526.	Earls Court	560.	Seven
527.	Seven	561.	Bradford
528.	England	562.	Nine
529.	Ten	563.	True
530.	Earls Court	564.	Three
531.	Eleven	565.	Eight
532.	Italy	566.	Six
533.	Three	567.	Twelve round points decision
534.	England	568.	Twelve round points decision
535.	Four		
536.	Two	569.	Twelve round draw
537.	Nuevo Laredo	570.	San Antonio
538.	Nine	571.	Twelve round draw
539.	False	572.	One
540.	Cardiff	573.	Six
541.	Twelve round points decision	574.	Featherweight
542.	False	575.	Five
543.	Russia	576.	One
544.	Three	577.	One
545.	Memphis	578.	Ten
546.	Twelve round points decision	579.	Six
547.	Enery's Ammer	580.	Four
548.	Light-Heavy	581.	One
549.	Six	582.	Mansfield
		583.	True

584.	Twelve round points decision	611.	Cruiserweight
585.	Germany	612.	Tommy Morrison
586.	May	613.	Tony Galento
587.	Lennox Lewis	614.	1964
588.	Six	615.	Bantamweight
589.	Twelve round points decision	616.	Barry McGuigan
590.	Six	617.	Twelve round points decision
591.	One	618.	Southwark
592.	Mississippi	619.	True
593.	Lennox Lewis	620.	False
594.	Twelve round points decision	621.	Two
595.	Twelve round points decision	622.	Twelve round points decision
596.	Six	623.	England
597.	Nine	624.	Twelve round points decision
598.	Three	625.	Billy Conn
599.	Twelve round points decision	626.	Twelve round points decision
600.	Welterweight	627.	Denmark
601.	False	628.	Five
		629.	Two
		630.	Five
		631.	England

ROUND SEVEN

		632.	One
602.	Puerto Rico	633.	True
603.	Joe Tetteh	634.	Twelve round points decision
604.	Heavy	635.	One
605.	1966	636.	Seven
606.	Twelve round points decision	637.	Yes
607.	Twelve round points decision	638.	Twelve round points decision
608.	Twelve round points decision	639.	Ten
609.	Thailand	640.	Points win for Luigi Camputaro
610.	Six	641.	Four

177

642.	Thailand	677.	Five
643.	Heavyweight	678.	Eight
644.	Seven	679.	Six
645.	Cardiff	680.	Eight
646.	True	681.	Ten
647.	No	682.	Seven
648.	No	683.	Six
649.	24	684.	True
650.	Two	685.	Twelve round points decision
651.	Twelve round points decision	686.	Mills Lane
652.	Twelve round points decision	687.	Las Vegas
		688.	True
653.	Argentina	689.	One
654.	WBO	690.	Seven
655.	Twelve round draw	691.	Bethnal Green
656.	False	692.	22
657.	False	693.	Ten
658.	Manchester	694.	Ten
659.	Three	695.	Two
660.	Three	696.	Nine
661.	Ten	697.	Twelve round points decision
662.	Nine	698.	Ten
663.	One	699.	Tony Orlando
664.	Tulsa	700.	Atlantic City
665.	England		
666.	Twelve round points decision		

ROUND EIGHT

667.	Ten		
668.	True	701.	Five
669.	Four	702.	Light-Heavyweight
670.	One	703.	Middleweight
671.	Five	704.	WBC
672.	Three	705.	Twelve round points decision
673.	Nine	706.	New Zealand
674.	False	707.	Seven
675.	Bethnal Green	708.	Five
676.	24		

709.	Atlantic City	740.	South Africa
710.	Seven	741.	IBF
711.	Twelve round points decision	742.	Glenn McCrory
		743.	1990
712.	Twelve round points decision	744.	Eight
		745.	South Africa
713.	Germany	746.	5ft. 7 inches
714.	Twelve round points decision	747.	Twelve round points decision
715.	Ten	748.	Germany
716.	Mexico City	749.	Two
717.	Twelve round points decision	750.	True
		751.	Twelve round points decision
718.	Japan		
719.	Four	752.	Four
720.	England	753.	Manchester
721.	Twenty Three	754.	A draw
722.	Twelve round points decision	755.	Six
		756.	Two
723.	10 November 1993	757.	Three
724.	Seven	758.	Fifteen
725.	24 February 1993	759.	Four
726.	Eleven	760.	Twelve round points decision
727.	Nine		
728.	Cardiff	761.	One
729.	Four	762.	Two
730.	Nine	763.	Five
731.	France	764.	False
732.	Twelve round points decision	765.	Puebla
		766.	Twelve round points decision
733.	Twelve round points decision	767.	Eight
734.	Reno	768.	100
735.	37	769.	Eleven
736.	Ten	770.	Twelve round points decision
737.	Ten		
738.	Two	771.	Twelve round points decision
739.	False		

772.	Five	803.	Twelve round points decision
773.	Hands of stone	804.	True
774.	One	805.	Twelve round points decision
775.	One	806.	One
776.	Seven	807.	Two
777.	Twelve round points decision	808.	America
778.	Seven	809.	80
779.	Seven	810.	False
780.	Six	811.	Twelve round points decision
781.	Cardiff	812.	Eight
782.	Twelve round points decision	813.	False
783.	Ron Lipton	814.	Eight
784.	Belfast	815.	Italy
785.	Twelve round points decision	816.	True
786.	Ireland	817.	Twelve round points decision
787.	One	818.	France
788.	Seven	819.	O.B.E.
789.	Three	820.	Twelve round points decision
790.	Seven	821.	Yes
791.	Nine	822.	Glasgow
792.	Britain	823.	Twelve round points decision
793.	True	824.	Scotland
794.	Four	825.	One
795.	Ten	826.	Twelve round points decision
796.	Cardiff	827.	Germany
797.	Six	828.	IBF
798.	Italy	829.	38

ROUND NINE

799.	Eight	830.	One
800.	Four	831.	Two
801.	One	832.	One
802.	Twelve round points decision	833.	False

834.	England	866.	Las Vegas
835.	Eight	867.	One
836.	Four	868.	Las Vegas
837.	Six	869.	Ten
838.	Bethnal Green	870.	Two
839.	Twelve round points decision	871.	Las Vegas
		872.	Ten
840.	Twelve round points decision	873.	Seven
		874.	Twelve
841.	Atlantic City	875.	False
842.	Three	876.	Cardiff
843.	Twelve round points decision	877.	Eight
		878.	17
844.	Twelve round points decision	879.	Twelve round points decision
845.	Earls Court	880.	Ten
846.	Yes	881.	One
847.	One	882.	Ten
848.	Twelve round points decision	883.	Six
		884.	Seven
849.	England	885.	False
850.	Six	886.	England
851.	One	887.	26
852.	Four	888.	Three
853.	Six	889.	Las Vegas
854.	Four	890.	False
855.	Seven	891.	One
856.	15	892.	Japan
857.	One	893.	Twelve round points decision
858.	Ten		
859.	Los Angeles	894.	6ft 6¼ inches
860.	12	895.	Light-Welterweight
861.	Four	896.	Middleweight
862.	Los Angeles	897.	Jake La Motta
863.	Six round technical draw	898.	Middleweight
864.	America	899.	Ten
865.	Twelve round points decision		

ROUND TEN

900. Cardiff
901. Pat Cowdell
902. Stopped in round eight
903. Twelve round points decision
904. 6ft 7 inches
905. Nine
906. Six
907. Twelve round points decision
908. Six
909. Two
910. Paul Hodkinson
911. Five
912. France
913. One
914. Six
915. Eight round draw
916. Twelve round points decision
917. Twelve round points decision
918. Reno
919. Chris Eubank
920. Eight
921. Two
922. Four
923. Twelve round points decision
924. Eleven
925. Las Vegas
926. Twelve round points decision
927. Mills Lane
928. Las Vegas
929. 35

930. Twelve round points decision
931. Joe Cortez
932. Ten
933. Twelve round points decision
934. England
935. Four
936. Eight
937. Arthur Mercante Snr.
938. America
939. 25
940. Five
941. America
942. 6ft 9 inches
943. Twelve round points decision
944. Twelve round points decision
945. Eight round technical points decision
946. One
947. Twelve round points decision
948. Twelve round points decision
949. Five
950. Paul Thomas
951. One
952. Twelve round points decision
953. England
954. Nine
955. Mickey Vann
956. England
957. Nine
958. Twelve round points decision

959.	Japan	995.	Ten
960.	Six	996.	Twelve round points decision
961.	Thailand		
962.	Twelve round points decision	997.	Robert Gonzales
		998.	Dortmund
963.	Belfast	999.	Nine
964.	Ten	1000.	Raul Caiz
965.	John Coyle	1001.	England
966.	Ireland		
967.	Russian		

ROUND ELEVEN

968.	Six		
969.	One	1002.	Five
970.	Thirteen	1003.	Laurence Cole
971.	Ten	1004.	Twelve round points decision
972.	Three		
973.	Dave Parris	1005.	Twelve
974.	Eight	1006.	Atlantic City
975.	False	1007.	Twelve round points decision
976.	A Draw		
977.	False	1008.	Thailand
978.	Three	1009.	1974
979.	Joe Cortez	1010.	Six
980.	Las Vegas	1011.	France
981.	Two	1012.	Twelve
982.	Richard Steele	1013.	Joe Cortez
983.	Las Vegas	1014.	Two
984.	False	1015.	Nine
985.	True	1016.	Three.
986.	Heavyweight	1017.	Richard Steele
987.	Three	1018.	Las Vegas
988.	Las Vegas	1019.	2 July
989.	Twelve round points decision	1020.	Two
		1021.	Mitch Halpern
990.	Toby Gibson	1022.	America
991.	Cardiff	1023.	No
992.	Two	1024.	Two
993.	One	1025.	Three
994.	Eleven		

1026. Twelve round points decision
1027. A draw
1028. Thailand
1029. Ten round points decision
1030. Twelve round points decision
1031. England
1032. Twelve round points decision
1033. Eight
1034. Four
1035. Twelve round points decision
1036. Phoenix
1037. Twelve round draw
1038. Mickey Vann
1039. One
1040. Thailand
1041. Seven
1042. Germany
1043. Four
1044. Seven
1045. Italy
1046. Twelve round points decision
1047. Twelve round points decision
1048. Twelve round points decision
1049. Four
1050. Twelve round points decision
1051. Dave Parris
1052. One
1053. John Coyle
1054. Twelve

1055. Joe Cortez
1056. Las Vegas
1057. Two